The Pocket Encyclopaedia of Spaceflight in Color

MANNED SPACECRAFT

The Pocket Encyclopaedia of
Spaceflight in Color

MANNED SPACECRAFT

by
KENNETH GATLAND
FRAS, FBIS

Illustrated by
JOHN W. WOOD
TONY MITCHELL

THE MACMILLAN COMPANY
NEW YORK

First Published in 1967
Copyright © Blandford Press Ltd.

Library of Congress catalog card number 67–22617

Printed and Bound in Great Britain
by Jarrold & Sons Ltd, Norwich

ACKNOWLEDGEMENTS

As a vice-president of the British Interplanetary Society it has been my pleasant duty to meet leading personalities concerned with space technology of both the United States and the Soviet Union, and to discuss with astronauts and cosmonauts their unique experiences of orbital flight.

The results of some of these encounters are given in the following pages where the attempt has been to interweave the human experience of spaceflight with the considerable technical achievement which the conquest of space represents. Opportunity has also been taken to sketch the steps that lie immediately ahead in manned spaceflight, including missions to the Moon and the development of the first orbiting laboratories.

A special feature of the present volume is the colour illustrations, some of which, like Mercury and Vostok, have been prepared after examination of actual hardware, and others from detailed drawings and photographs supplied by companies concerned with project development. The principal artist, John Wood, has worked with me for the past twenty years (following our association in the design department of Hawker Aircraft Limited at Kingston-upon-Thames) and is now among the best known in the aerospace field. He was assisted in the present work by Tony Mitchell, another Hawker protégé, whose own talents for aerospace illustration are fast becoming recognized.

Special mention must also be made of North American Aviation artists whose excellent series of impressions of the Apollo lunar mission appear on pages 77–81, 83, 84, 87 and 91. My good friend W. A. 'Bill' Dunn of the United States Information Service in London supplied the transparencies showing actual U.S. spacecraft, the Kennedy Space Center and astronaut photographs taken from orbit. The publishers join me in expressing special appreciation to both these sources.

Particular thanks are also due to the following for photographs and technical information: McDonnell Company (Mercury, Gemini and ATDA); North American Aviation (X-15A-2, Apollo command, service and adapter modules); Grumman Aircraft Engineering Corporation (Apollo lunar module); The Martin Company (Titan 2 and lifting bodies SV-5D and SV-5P); Northrop Corporation (lifting bodies M2-F2 and HL-10); United Technology Center (lateral boosters Titan 3C and 3M); Lockheed Aircraft Corporation (Agena target vehicle); General Electric Company of the USA (ALSEP); Ryan Aeronautical Company (Apollo landing radar); and Douglas Missile & Space Systems Division (Manned Orbiting Research Laboratory). I am also grateful to Kenneth Munson for certain data relating to the X-15 and U-2 aircraft.

Once again it is a pleasure to record appreciation of the flow of technical material from the National Aeronautics and Space Administration in Washington, and the ready assistance offered by NASA to researchers in this field. Definitive information on Soviet space progress is characteristically more difficult to obtain; but even here there has been evidence of improved lines of communication. I am particularly indebted to Mrs Iris Smith of the Novosti Press Agency in London for assistance in obtaining photographs and data relating to Soviet space technology.

All launch and orbital data are those officially released by the country of origin. Where orbital parameters are given they normally refer to the initial orbit. My earlier books, *Spacecraft and Boosters*, Vols. 1 and 2 (Iliffe Books Ltd), detailing space launchings of 1961 and 1962, have been helpful in arriving at qualified data. The following additional sources have been freely consulted: *Flight International*, *Aviation Week & Space Technology*, *Spaceflight* (a monthly publication of the British Interplanetary Society), and *Space Log* (edited by Thomas L. Branigan for TRW Space Technology Laboratories).

Lastly, much is owed to my wife Doreen whose unstinting efforts in typing the manuscript contributed greatly to the ability to produce the text in little more than two months.

For the convenience of international editions the 80-page colour section is bound at the front of the book. The captions which appear on the colour pages are amplified in Chapter Four where full details of the subjects are given with appropriate reference numbers.

KENNETH W. GATLAND

CONTENTS

ACKNOWLEDGEMENTS   5

INTRODUCTION   8

THE COLOR PAGES   17

1 RED STAR IN SPACE   97

2 BRIDGE TO THE MOON   141

3 THE LUNAR EXPLORERS   182

4 SPACECRAFT IN FOCUS   196

THE LAUNCH VEHICLES   248

GLOSSARY   253

INDEX   254

INTRODUCTION

Money spent on the advancement of knowledge is seldom wasted. Given time, the investment nearly always reaps a rich reward, often in the most unexpected directions.

Astronautics – the science and technology of spaceflight – is likely to be no exception. Combining as it does almost every scientific and technical discipline, it has already become a 'spearhead technology' stimulating the development of new materials and processes of manufacture. All the time, because of space activity, there is a steady advancement in such basic fields as metals, ceramics, plastics, micro-electronics, power generation, industrial management, and many more. The effects on industry in general are evolutionary and largely unseen, but for all that they may be expected to have the widest significance for twentieth-century man.

There may even be important medical benefits. The close attention now being paid to the work of the human body under space conditions is resulting in more data being amassed on vital physiological functions – particularly concerning the circulatory system under stress – than in decades of conventional medicine. Techniques learnt in space, such as the monitoring of bodily functions by telemetric sensors (e.g. heart-rate, pulse, and respiration), are starting to revolutionize medical instrumentation in hospitals. Semi-automated hospitals, where a patient's physiological reactions are automatically reported to master consoles, are already in prospect which both alert the medical staff and provide computerized data on the patient's condition.

However, new and perhaps even more exciting opportunities are about to open, for medical research could benefit from the close attention that space scientists are paying to the living cell in terms of the search for life on other planets. The automated biological laboratory, which the American Voyager spacecraft is to land on Mars in the 1970s, will have both soil sampling and air sampling apparatus for checking on the presence of bacteria and reporting findings to Earth.

In this area of advanced biology the interests of space science and medical research may merge to the benefit of mankind, for a greater understanding of the properties of the living cell is fundamental to winning the battle against malignant disease. It is interesting and vitally significant that important experiments concerning the structure of living matter are now taking place in research centres devoted to space problems.

If these are the 'hidden' benefits of space research, much more is nakedly apparent. Indeed, the most obvious is already taken for granted in terms of satellites that now allow television to span continents and oceans. The development of satellite communications in the first decade of the space age has been little short of miraculous; and when we see programmes on our TV screens relayed across the Atlantic we little think of the small box of high-grade electronics working unattended in the hostile environment of space that makes it all possible. Even Arthur C. Clarke, a former chairman of the British Interplanetary Society, who first proposed the synchronous-orbit TV satellite in 1945, could scarcely have imagined the standards of reliability now being achieved in space electronics.

The achievement, of course, extends far beyond communications. Satellites warning of the approach of hurricanes and typhoons – as well as performing routine global weather survey – are in regular operation. Others serving as 'radio-stars' for the precise navigation of ships and aircraft have been demonstrated, and the future is bright for a combination of these systems in the form of multipurpose spacecraft.

If all this has been possible in the first ten years of space technology, what will twenty or thirty years of development have in store? It is not difficult to predict that our planet will have a network of space communications serving the interests of governments, trade and industry. Computer-controlled information banks, flashing the most up-to-date data of all kinds by satellite to subscribers around the world, have already been suggested, which may offer immense opportunities for commerce and education.

One other important development can also be forecast. This

is the direct-broadcasting satellite poised in geo-stationary orbit beaming radio and television directly to domestic aerials. Such powerful satellites, dispensing with costly ground terminals and cross-country relay stations, will depend on cheaply produced dish aerials pointed skywards to intercept the signals coming to them directly from space. In this way programmes beamed to a satellite from a single ground transmitter will be re-transmitted over a vast area.

Apart from the utility of such satellites in developed parts of the world, they could become one of the most effective methods of bringing education to community centres in the emergent countries.

The growth of supersonic air travel, first over the Atlantic and then the Pacific, is also likely to depend heavily on satellites for air-traffic control, ensuring the maximum of safety for the international commuter.

None of these techniques demands radical advances from systems already developed in the first space decade, and their influence is likely to be much wider than our present imaginings.

But even this is not the limit of the space age potential. Those who strove to build the science of astronautics in many countries, who were filled with the desire to promote a deeper under-standing of the Universe through interplanetary exploration, have always regarded themselves as members of a greater international family. It is therefore heartening that space activity, rather than adding to the human burden in terms of armaments, is actually helping to reduce tensions.

In a very real sense space travel is sweeping aside national boundaries, making closed societies more difficult and breaking down national distrust. Eventually, the space race that grew out of the East–West rivalries of the 'fifties must give way to col-laboration; and it may well promote the climate for at least a degree of disarmament.

Already the United Nations treaty on outer space, signed in 1967 by countries of both East and West, bans weapons of mass destruction from outer space and provides for equal access to the Moon and other celestial bodies by all nations. Out of this could grow collaboration in the exploration of the Moon. When it becomes technically possible, in principle there is nothing to prevent the United States and the Soviet Union, under an agreed programme, combining in a joint logistics operation to carry prefabricated parts to the Moon for the development of an international lunar base.

A lead in this direction, in fact, was given by the late President Kennedy. Addressing the U.N. General Assembly on 20 September 1963, he said: 'Why . . . should man's first flight to the Moon be a matter of national competition? Why should the United States and the Soviet Union, in preparing such expeditions, become involved in immense duplications of research, construction and expenditure? Surely we should explore whether the scientists and astronauts of our two countries – indeed of all the world – cannot work together in the conquest of space, sending some day in this decade to the Moon not the representatives of a single nation but the representatives of all our countries.'

Although the suggestion lacked a formula for combining East and West space development resources, it expressed the feelings of many people. In an atmosphere of reducing international tensions, at some future stage, it may be possible to achieve a degree of technological co-operation; and possibly the best chances lie in the direction of expensive projects involving logistics supply – the lunar base and manned interplanetary exploration.

As a first step – as Colonel John Stapp has proposed to the International Academy of Astronautics – it might be possible to develop an international orbiting laboratory. This would not involve the assembly of a single space-station in Earth-orbit but rather the orbital grouping of a number of spacecraft in conjunction with a 'dormitory' module. The various components, put up from launch centres in both the United States and the Soviet Union, would serve different functions. For example, one could work in astronomy, another in biology and another in meteorology and Earth-observation. And each would benefit from the others in terms of logistics support, equipment repair and astronaut safety. Astronaut-scientists would move between the different vehicles in a kind of 'space-taxi' using techniques of docking

already developed in the Gemini and Apollo programmes. As
will be seen in Chapter Four, the modular assembly of an
orbiting laboratory is being investigated in the Apollo Applications Programme.

The prospects of this type of development are considerable.
While scientific satellites and space probes have begun to
revolutionize our understanding of the Universe, cameras and
spectral sensors turned on the Earth itself have shown the promise
of new opportunities for assessing the world's natural resources.
The National Aeronautics and Space Administration has defined
more than 200 Earth-related experiments that could be performed
from a manned orbiting laboratory including cartography (mapping), geology, oceanography, water management, ice survey,
agriculture, meteorology and other studies unique to the space
environment.

Dr Wernher von Braun, technical director of the Marshall
Spaceflight Center in Huntsville, Alabama, has written en-
thusiastically of these prospects. Everywhere he goes, man cuts
trees, tills soil, builds houses, factories and roads. All this random
activity is detectable from space. This information collated with
Earth-based information can be used to assess the world's
burgeoning population and future needs. From the high-ground
of space it may be possible to detect crop disease. Black stain
rust, von Braun points out, is difficult to detect in its early stages.
Remote sensors can spot the rust several days earlier than a man
who is standing on the ground.

Using similar remote techniques it should be possible to discover water and mineral imbalance in the soil, leading to better
use of land in agriculture. By measuring minute differences in
soil temperature it may be possible to detect underwater rivers,
or measure snowfall and spring thaws helpful to the management
of water in storage lakes. Life patterns in the seas, and feeding
grounds for fish, may also be discernible.

Many of these remote sensing techniques are possible because
of the prior development of military reconnaissance and surveillance satellites. Observations made by the astronauts themselves
have contributed important information.

When I discussed the concept of the international orbiting laboratory with Dr von Braun, he thought it inconceivable that such unique opportunities for research should be restricted to scientists of the richer nations. He envisaged the possibility of grants being established on the pattern of Antarctic exploration, whereby graduate scientists of all countries could qualify, after special training, to conduct research aboard space vehicles.

Whether or not this degree of co-operation comes about after the 'space race' is over, only time will tell. It is conceivable that, despite different ideologies, the routine and arduous task of exploiting space and the Moon for scientific and economic purposes will induce nations to work together instead of in competition. If it does the best hopes of those who laid the foundations for astronautics will have been realized.

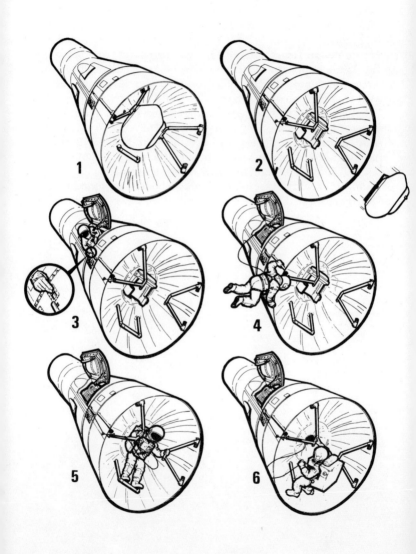

The most ambitious extra-vehicular activity (EVA) experiment planned for a Gemini astronaut involved use of two modules, a chest pack Emergency Life Support System (ELSS) and a backpack Modular Manœuvring Unit (MMU). Together with the Gemini pressure suit these comprised the Astronaut Manœuvring Unit (AMU) shown on page 59, a system that is essentially a miniature human spacecraft. The experiment, which was not completed during the Gemini 9 mission, required the EVA astronaut to make his way from the Gemini cabin to the back of the adapter module with the use of hand-holds to don the MMU backpack. Pictures show the intended sequence of operations: 1. MMU stowage at back of adapter module; 2. Ejection of cover plate; 3. EVA astronaut extends hand-rail; 4. Astronaut transfers to adapter module; 5. Seats into MMU and fixes 100 ft tether extension; 6. Leaves with MMU backpack for manœuvre experiments adjacent to spacecraft. Results of the experiment which had to be curtailed are given in Chapter Two, page 173.

The Color Pages

The 80 color pages which follow illustrate United States and Soviet manned spacecraft, launch vehicles, launch sites, spacesuits, views from orbit, and the Apollo lunar mission. The reference number for each subject corresponds to the appropriate text matter. An index appears on pages 254–256.

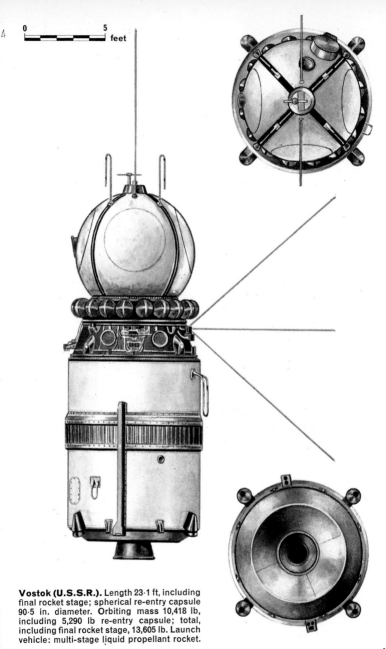

Vostok (U.S.S.R.). Length 23·1 ft, including final rocket stage; spherical re-entry capsule 90·5 in. diameter. Orbiting mass 10,418 lb, including 5,290 lb re-entry capsule; total, including final rocket stage, 13,605 lb. Launch vehicle: multi-stage liquid propellant rocket.

17

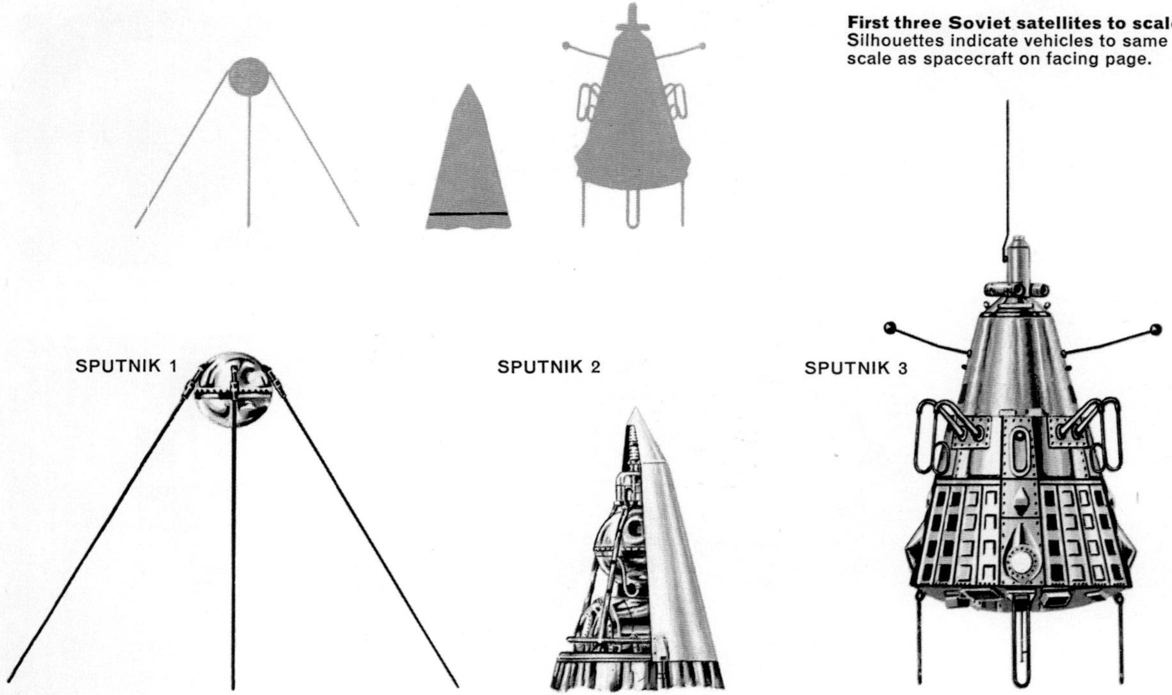

First three Soviet satellites to scale. Silhouettes indicate vehicles to same scale as spacecraft on facing page.

SPUTNIK 3

SPUTNIK 2

SPUTNIK 1

Vostok and Voskhod spacecraft complete with jettisonable nose fairings and final stage rockets. Note similarity between final stages of Lunik and Vostok launchers. (Voskhod drawing is provisional.)

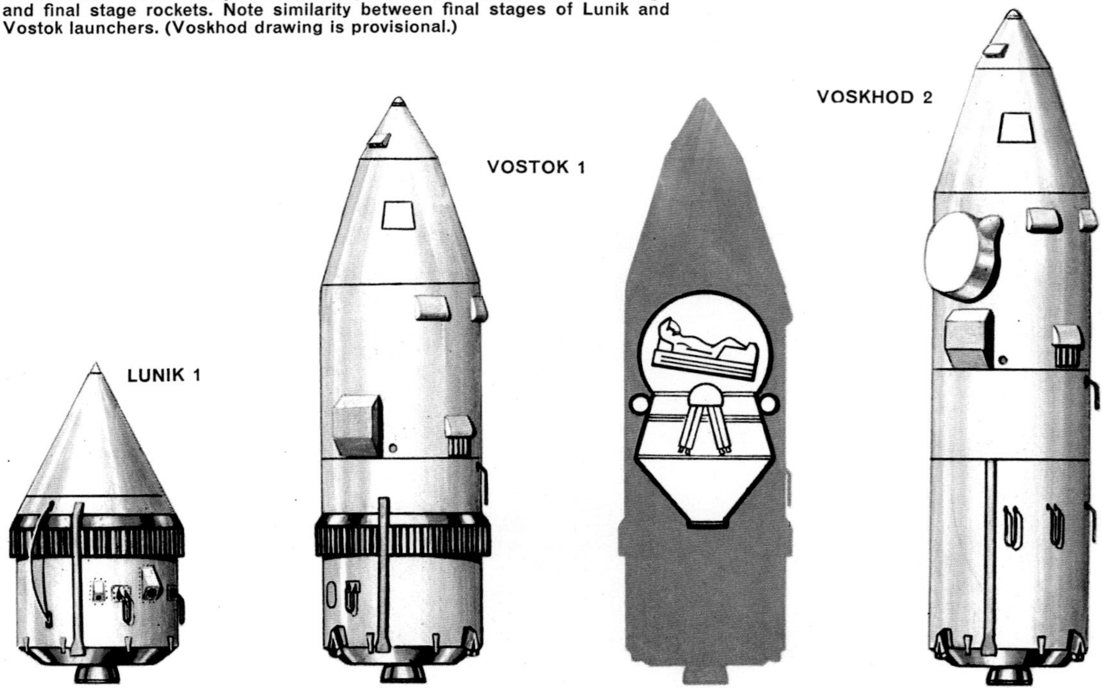

VOSKHOD 2

VOSTOK 1

VOSTOK 1

LUNIK 1

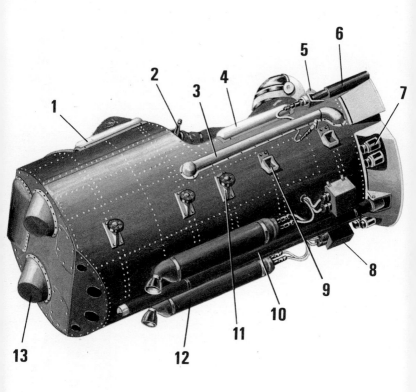

(Above) **Vostok ejection seat.** *(Key):* 1. Leg pad; 2. Handle for shoulder harness; 3. Conduit; 4. Arm pad; 5. socket connector; 6. Back plate ejector; 7. Aneroid pressure sensors; 8. Radio beacons; 9. Seat guides; 10. Piston; 11. Seat runners; 12. Ejection rockets; 13. Seat buffers.

(Right) **Vostok escape hatch.** *Key:* 1. Nose fairing; 2. Fairing aperture; 3. Capsule support flange; 4. Hatch flange; 5. Cosmonaut's ejection seat; 6. Re-entry capsule; 7. Equipment module containing retro-rocket; 8. Final rocket stage.

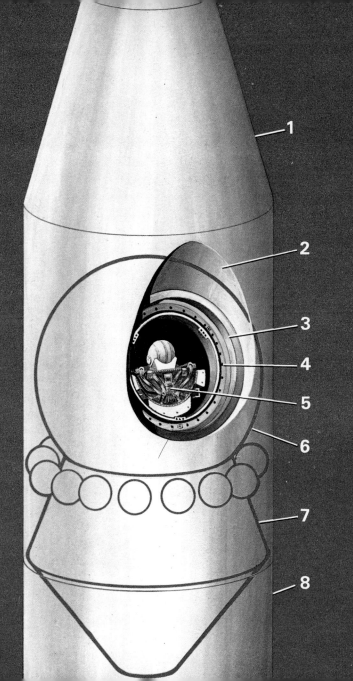

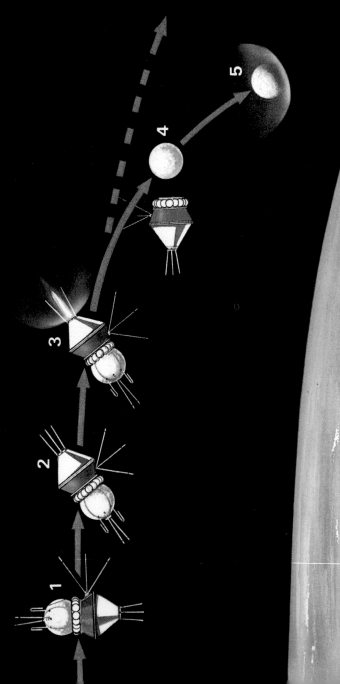

Vostok re-entry. *Key*: 1. Spacecraft in orbit; 2. Oriented with solar cells towards sun; 3. Retro-fire; 4. Capsule separates; 5. Re-entry heating.

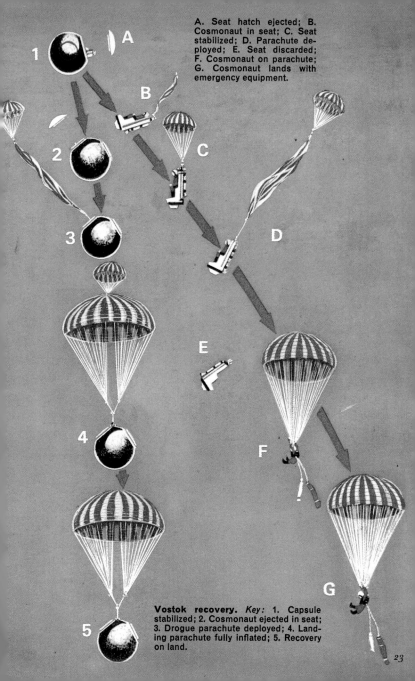

A. Seat hatch ejected; B. Cosmonaut in seat; C. Seat stabilized; D. Parachute deployed; E. Seat discarded; F. Cosmonaut on parachute; G. Cosmonaut lands with emergency equipment.

Vostok recovery. *Key:* 1. Capsule stabilized; 2. Cosmonaut ejected in seat; 3. Drogue parachute deployed; 4. Landing parachute fully inflated; 5. Recovery on land.

23

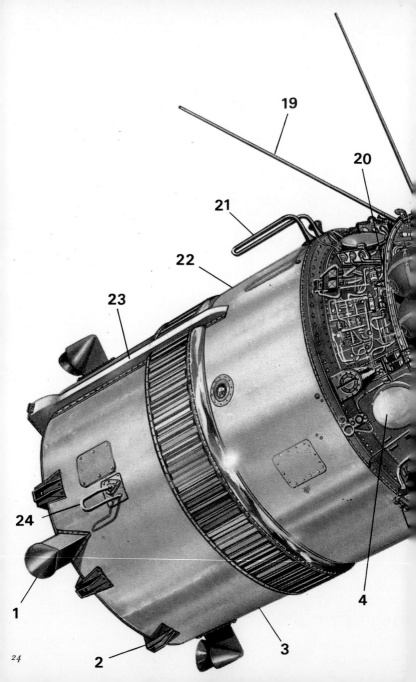

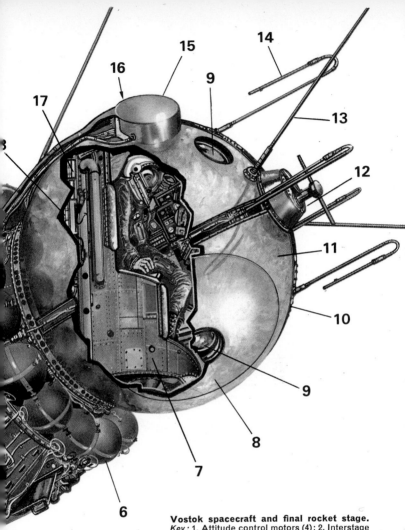

Vostok spacecraft and final rocket stage.
Key: 1. Attitude control motors (4); 2. Interstage attachments (8); 3. Final stage rocket; 4. Access hatch; 5. Vernier nozzles; 6. Oxygen and nitrogen storage bottles (16); 7. Cosmonaut's ejection seat; 8. Equipment inspection hatch; 9. Portholes; 10. Tensioning bands holding re-entry capsule; 11. Spherical re-entry capsule with ablative heat shield; 12. Electronics package; 13. Whip aerials 11 ft long (2); 14. Control command aerials (4); 15. Multiplex connector; 16. Ejection seat hatch (unseen at rear); 17. Ejection seat rails; 18. Ejection seat rocket motors; 19. Whip aerials (4); 20. Electrical harness; 21. 'Paper-clip' command aerial; 22. Rocket stage extension (shrouding retro-rocket of equipment module); 23. External conduit; 24. VHF aerial.

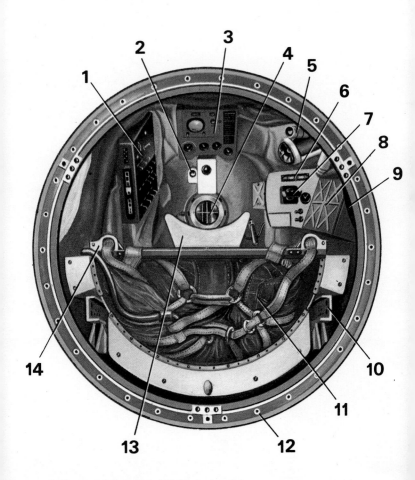

Vostok interior (as seen through ejection seat hatch). *Key:* 1. Switch panel;
2. Television camera; 3. Instrument panel with revolving Earth-globe; 4. Porthole, incorporating 'Vzor' optical orientation device; 5. Mirror; 6. Radio;
7. Manual control handle; 8. Food container; 9. Multiplex connector; 10. Ejection
seat rail; 11. Seat drogue and parachute; 12. Threaded sockets for hatch cover;
13. Ejection seat headrest; 14. Anchorage for parachute harness.

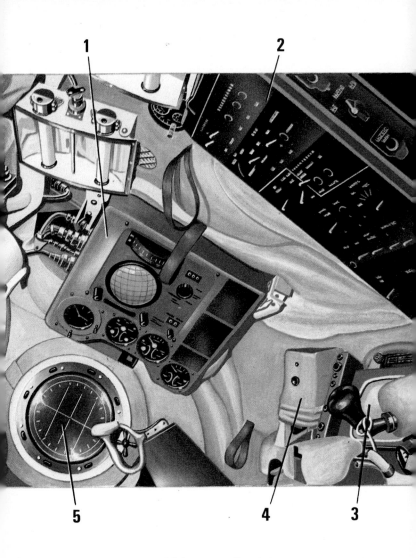

Voskhod 2 interior, near left-hand seat. *Key:* 1. Instrument panel with revolving Earth-globe; 2. Switch panel; 3. Television screen; 4. Television camera; 5. Porthole, incorporating 'Vzor' optical orientation device.

Soviet space activity. *Key:* 1. German collective, Khimki (1946); 2. German collective engine tests, Seliger Lake (1948); 3. U.S. Air Force radar surveillance, Samsun (Turkey); 4. Kapustin Yar cosmodrome (1947); 5. Tyuratam/Baikonur launch complex (1957); 6. Northern cosmodrome (1966); 7. Sounding rocket base,

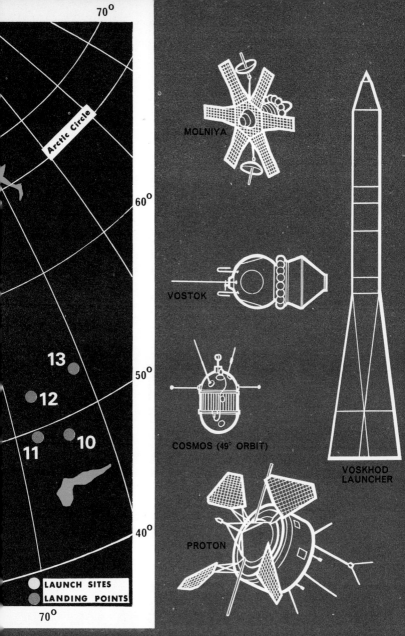

Franz Josef Land; following are landing places of early Soviet spacecraft:
8. Vostok 1; 9. Vostok 2; 10. Vostok 3; 11. Vostok 4; 12. Vostok 5; 13. Vostok 6;
14. Voskhod 1; 15. Voskhod 2.

Astronaut Walter Schirra's **Mercury capsule Sigma 7** installed on the Atlas-D launch vehicle at Cape Canaveral (now Cape Kennedy).

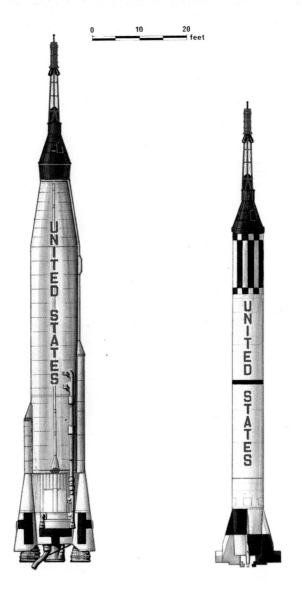

0   10   20
feet

(Left) **Mercury-Atlas.** Length, including escape tower, 94 ft 4 in.; tank diameter 10 ft; width over boost fairing 16 ft. Launch weight 260,000 lb; launch thrust 367,000 lb. *(Right)* **Mercury-Redstone.** Length, including escape tower, 83 ft; diameter 5 ft 10 in. Launch weight 66,000 lb; launch thrust 78,000 lb.

McDonnell Mercury. Length, including retro-pack, escape rocket and aerodynamic 'spike', 25 ft 11 in.; heat shield diameter 74·5 in. Typical weights (MA-6):
at launch 4,265 lb; in orbit 2,987 lb; on recovery 2,422 lb. Launch vehicle:
modified Atlas-D.

Mercury 'off-the-pad abort'. *Key :* 1. Escape rocket separates spacecraft; 2. Escape tower jettisons; 3. Drogue parachute deploys; 4. Capsule stabilizes; 5. Main parachute opens and landing bag deploys; 6. Awaits ocean retrieval.

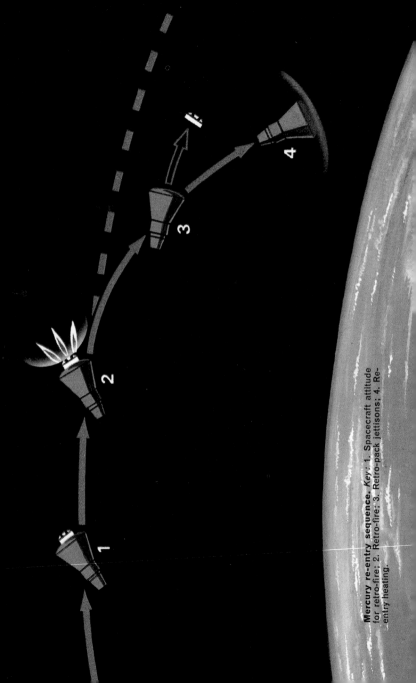

Mercury re-entry sequence. *Key:* 1. Spacecraft attitude for retro-fire; 2. Retro-fire; 3. Retro-pack jettisons; 4. Re-entry heating.

Mercury recovery sequence. *Key:*
1. Re-entry attitude; 2. Drogue deploys;
3. Main parachute deploys/parachute
'can' jettisons; 4. Main parachute reefed;
5. Landing parachute fully open and
landing bag deployed; 6. Awaits ocean
retrieval.

Gemini 6 with astronauts Walter Schirra and Thomas Stafford heads for an appointment in orbit with Gemini 7 on 15 December 1965. Within hours the two craft were to rendezvous at 17,500 m.p.h., keeping station only a few feet apart.

36

(Left) **Gemini-Titan 2.** Length 109 ft; diameter 10 ft. Launch weight 340,000 lb. First stage thrust 430,000 lb; second stage thrust 100,000 lb. *(Right)* **MOL-Titan 3M** (provisional). Length 155 ft; Titan core diameter 10 ft; seven-segment lateral solid boosters 110 ft long × 10 ft diameter.

```
0          10          20
|_____|_____| feet
```

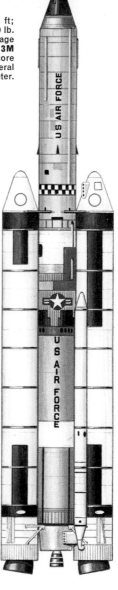

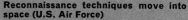

Reconnaissance techniques move into space (U.S. Air Force)
Manned Orbiting Laboratory. Length, c/w retrieval spacecraft, 54 ft; less spacecraft 41 ft; diameter 10 ft. Cameras, radiation sensors and other classified equipment.

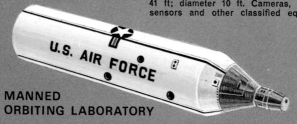

MANNED ORBITING LABORATORY

SAMOS

Samos (various Agena configuration). Length 22–30 ft; diameter 5 ft. Optical and electronic (Ferrett) surveillance equipment. Exposed photographic film returned in ejectable capsule.

U.2.

U-2 (various types). WU-2A illustrated. Length 49 ft 7 in.; span 80 ft. U-2A and B had reconnaissance cameras and electronic sensors; WU-2A used for high-altitude radiation sampling.

Titan 3C is launched on 3 November 1966, with a mock-up of the Manned Orbiting Laboratory (MOL) made from a Titan 2 fuel tank; in the extreme nose is a Gemini spacecraft. MOL development vehicles employ the more powerful Titan 3M as launcher.

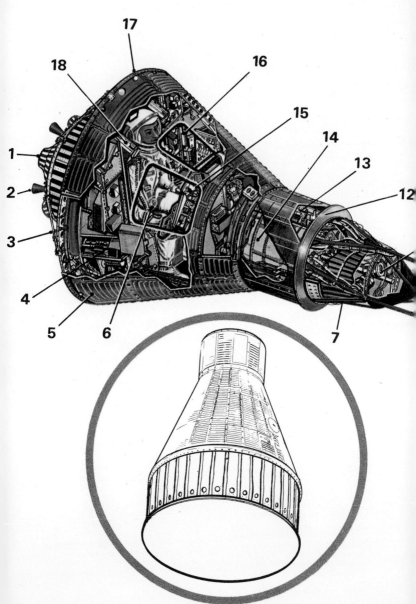

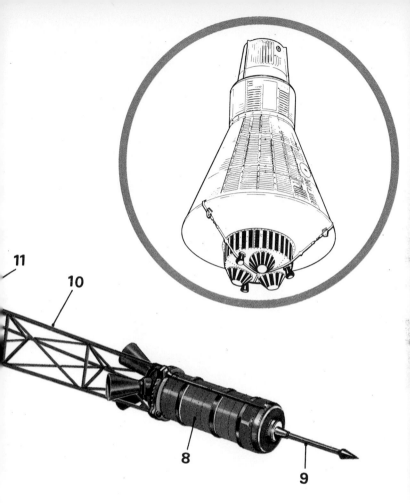

McDonnell Mercury. *Key:* 1. Retro-pack; 2. Separation rockets; 3. Retro-rocket retaining straps; 4. Attitude thrusters; 5. Skin shingles; 6. Hatch; 7. Drogue parachute stowage; 8. Emergency escape rocket; 9. Aerodynamic spike; 10. Escape tower; 11. Horizon sensors; 12. Aerodynamic fairing; 13. Attitude thrusters; 14. Main and reserve landing parachutes; 15. Instrument panels; 16. Window; 17. Heat shield; 18. Astronaut's couch.

(Inset, right) shows the ablative heat shield and retro-pack which also contained spacecraft separation rockets;

(inset, left) shows the heat shield dropped to extend the pneumatic landing bag.

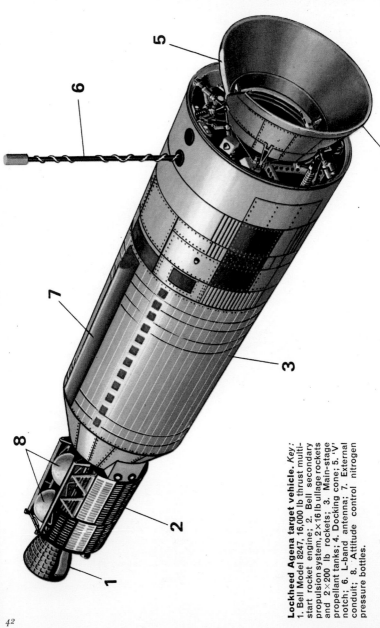

Lockheed Agena target vehicle. *Key:* 1. Bell Model 8247, 16,000 lb thrust multi-start rocket engine; 2. Bell secondary propulsion system, 2×16 lb ullage rockets and 2×200 lb rockets; 3. Main-stage propellant tanks; 4. Docking cone; 5. 'V' notch; 6. L-band antenna; 7. External conduit; 8. Attitude control nitrogen pressure bottles.

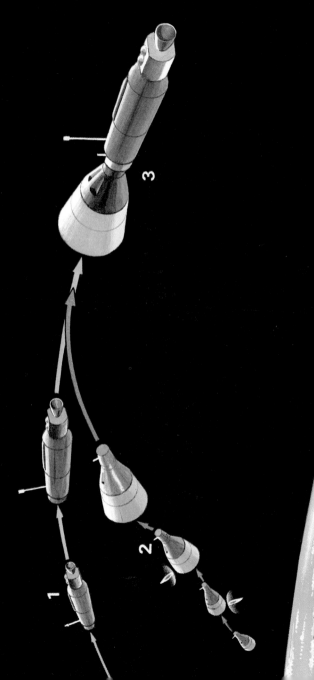

Gemini rendezvous and docking.
Key: 1. Agena target vehicle; 2. Gemini radar-controlled manœuvre; 3. Gemini docking under manual sighting and control.

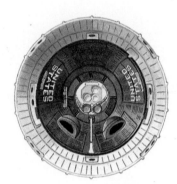

0   5
         feet

McDonnell Gemini. Length complete with retrograde and equipment modules
18 ft 5 in.; maximum diameter 10 ft; small end diameter 39 in.; length retrograde
and equipment modules 7 ft 6 in. Heat shield diameter 90 in. Weight: 7,100 to
8,350 lb. Launch vehicle: modified Titan 2.

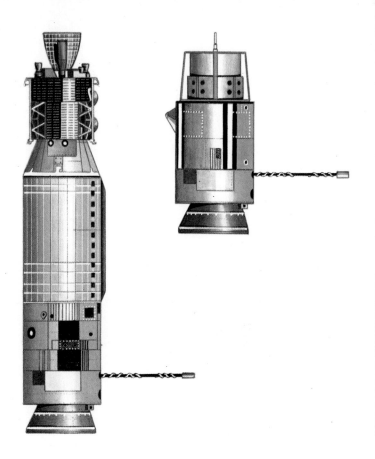

0   5
feet

(Left) **Lockheed Agena rendezvous target.** Length 25 ft 7 in.; diameter 5 ft. Weight, fuelled, in orbit 7,000 lb. Main engine thrust 16,000 lb. *(Right)* **McDonnell A.T.D.A.** Length 10 ft 11 in.; diameter 5 ft. Typical weights: at launch 2,400 lb; in orbit 1,700 lb. No independent propulsion. Launch vehicle, both targets, modified Atlas-D (overall height with Agena 104 ft; with A.T.D.A. 95 ft 6 in.).

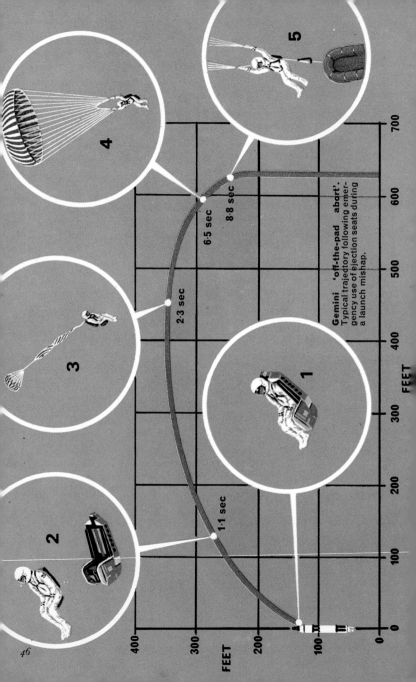

1

2

3

4

5

1·1 sec

2·3 sec

6·5 sec

8·8 sec

Gemini 'off-the-pad' abort'.
Typical trajectory following emergency use of ejection seats during a launch mishap.

FEET

100   200   300   400   500   600   700

FEET

100   200   300   400

46

Gemini emergency escape following separation from Titan booster at higher altitude. *Key*: 1. Seat ejection; 2. Astronaut free of seat; 3. 'Ballute' stabilizer inflates; 4. Drogue deploys/ballute jettisons; 5. Landing parachute fully inflated.

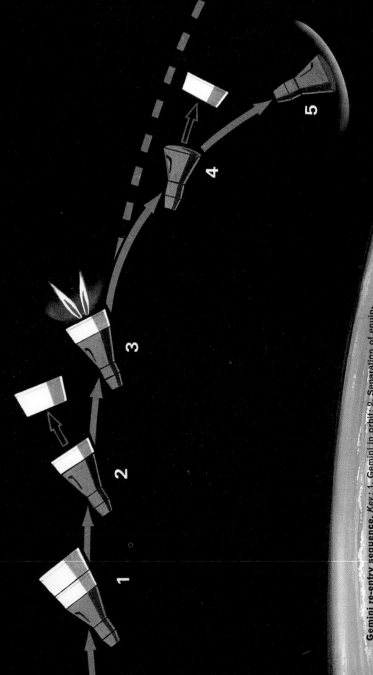

Gemini re-entry sequence. *Key*: 1. Gemini in orbit; 2. Separation of equipment module; 3. Retro-fire; 4. Separation of retro-module; 5. Re-entry heating.

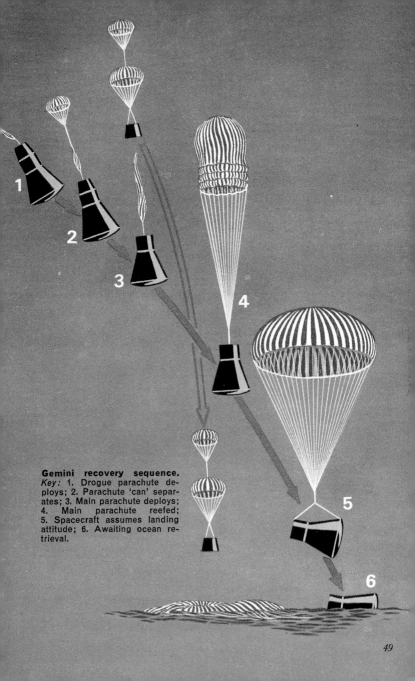

Gemini recovery sequence.
Key: 1. Drogue parachute deploys; 2. Parachute 'can' separates; 3. Main parachute deploys; 4. Main parachute reefed; 5. Spacecraft assumes landing attitude; 6. Awaiting ocean retrieval.

(Top) **Gemini 7** as seen from the window of Gemini 6 during the first space rendezvous; *(bottom)* instant before docking with an Agena target vehicle. The view from Gemini 10.

Gemini 11 astronauts look down on the Agena target vehicle with which their own craft is loosely connected by a 100 ft tether. They were orbiting over Lower California near La Paz.

(Top) Edward White becomes the first American to leave a spacecraft in orbit on 3 June 1965. *(Bottom)* Richard Gordon straddles the cylindrical neck of Gemini 11 to fix a Dacron tether between his craft and the docked Agena.

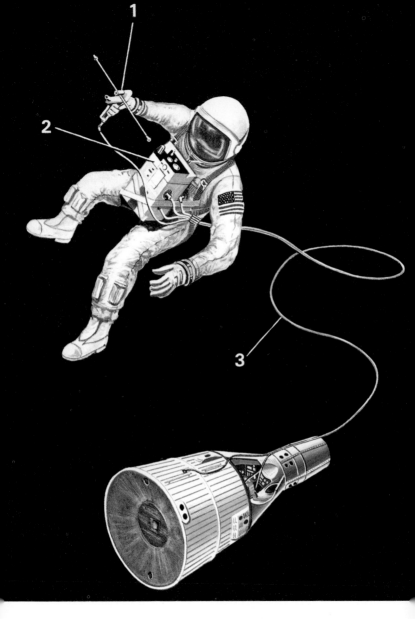

Extra-vehicular astronaut. Helmet visor thinly coated with gold protects the eyes from intense sunlight in space but allows clear visibility. *Key:* 1. Hand-held manœuvring unit; 2. Extra-vehicular life support system; 3. Astronaut umbilical tether.

North-Western Australia as seen from Gemini 11 from 850 miles. At extreme left is the city of Perth; *top left*, Indian Ocean; *left* of antenna tip, North West Cape; *top*, Timor Sea and *extreme top right*, Indonesia. In the *foreground*, near antenna stem, is the Great Sandy Desert.

Red Sea and Gulf of Aden from Gemini 11. Antenna points to Red Sea, Saudi Arabia is above; Ethiopia below and Indian Ocean at extreme right. It is instructive to compare these photographs with appropriate maps in an atlas.

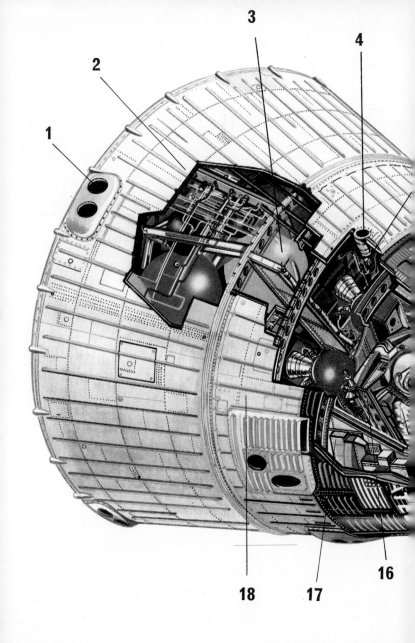

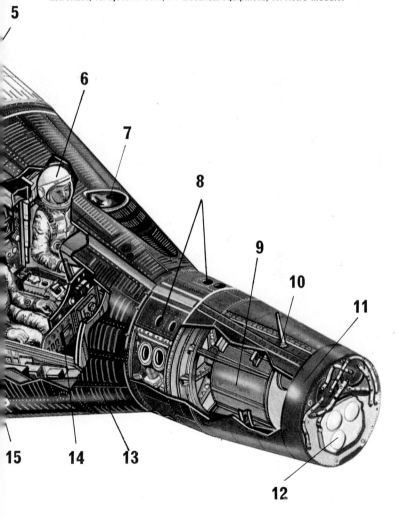

McDonnell Gemini. *Key:* 1. Attitude control thrusters; 2. Equipment module; 3. Fuel, oxidant and pressure tanks; 4. Manœuvre thrusters; 5. Retro-rockets; 6. Command pilot; 7. Window; 8. Re-entry attitude thrusters; 9. Landing parachute stowage; 10. Docking bar; 11. Rendezvous radar; 12. Drogue parachute stowage; 13. Re-entry module; 14. Instrument panels; 15. Pilot/EVA astronaut; 16. Ejection seat; 17. Electrical equipment; 18. Retro-module.

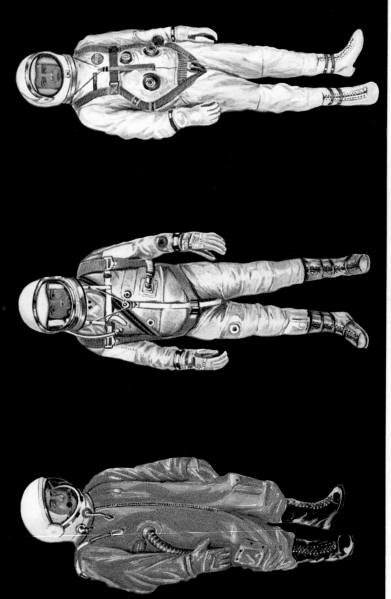

Early spacesuits: (*left to right*) Vostok; Mercury and Gemini. In the case of Vostok the actual pressure garment was hidden by a loose-fitting coverall.

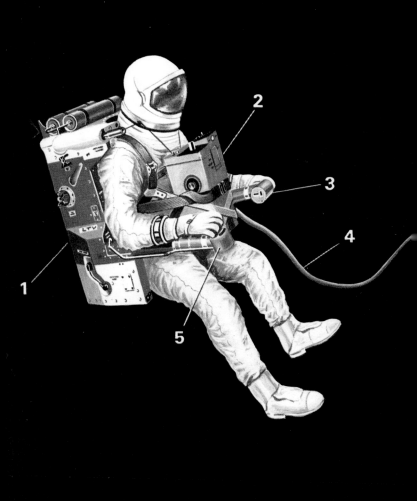

Astronaut Manœuvring Unit. *Key:* 1. Modular manœuvring unit; 2. Emergency life support system; 3. Arm-rest and hand control; 4. Tether; 5. Arm-rest and hand control.

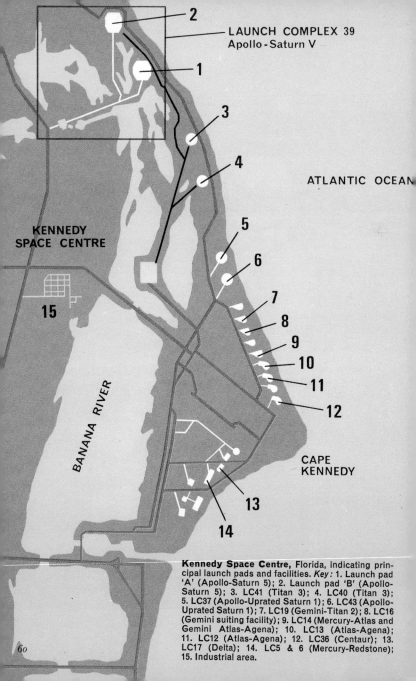

LAUNCH COMPLEX 39
Apollo-Saturn V

ATLANTIC OCEAN

KENNEDY
SPACE CENTRE

BANANA RIVER

CAPE
KENNEDY

Kennedy Space Centre, Florida, indicating principal launch pads and facilities. *Key:* 1. Launch pad 'A' (Apollo-Saturn 5); 2. Launch pad 'B' (Apollo-Saturn 5); 3. LC41 (Titan 3); 4. LC40 (Titan 3); 5. LC37 (Apollo-Uprated Saturn 1); 6. LC43 (Apollo-Uprated Saturn 1); 7. LC19 (Gemini-Titan 2); 8. LC16 (Gemini suiting facility); 9. LC14 (Mercury-Atlas and Gemini Atlas-Agena); 10. LC13 (Atlas-Agena); 11. LC12 (Atlas-Agena); 12. LC36 (Centaur); 13. LC17 (Delta); 14. LC5 & 6 (Mercury-Redstone); 15. Industrial area.

Cape Kennedy as viewed from orbit. Note launch pads along the coast, causeways over Banana River and Apollo launch pads on Merritt Island. The picture was taken by Gemini 5 astronaut Charles Conrad from 130 miles altitude.

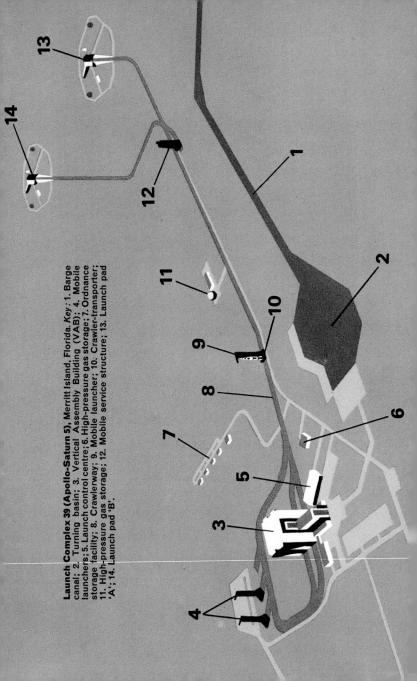

Launch Complex 39 (Apollo–Saturn 5), Merritt Island, Florida. *Key*: 1. Barge canal; 2. Turning basin; 3. Vertical Assembly Building (VAB); 4. Mobile launchers; 5. Launch control centre; 6. High-pressure gas storage; 7. Ordnance storage facility; 8. Crawlerway; 9. Mobile launcher; 10. Crawler-transporter; 11. High-pressure gas storage; 12. Mobile service structure; 13. Launch pad 'A'; 14. Launch pad 'B'.

The **Saturn 5 launch complex** on Merritt Island, Florida, with the Vehicle Assembly Building in the foreground. In the far distance are launch pads 'A' and 'B' for project Apollo.

63

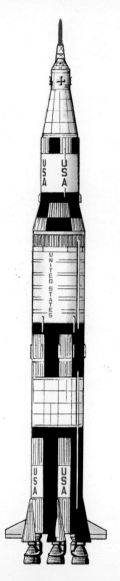

(Left) **Apollo-Uprated Saturn 1.** Length including spacecraft escape tower 224 ft; maximum diameter 21 ft 8 in. Launch weight 1,300,000 lb; launch thrust 1,600,000 lb. *(Right)* **Apollo-Saturn 5.** Length including spacecraft escape tower 364 ft 6 in.; maximum diameter 33 ft. Launch weight 6,000,000+ lb; launch thrust 7,500,000 lb.

0   50
feet

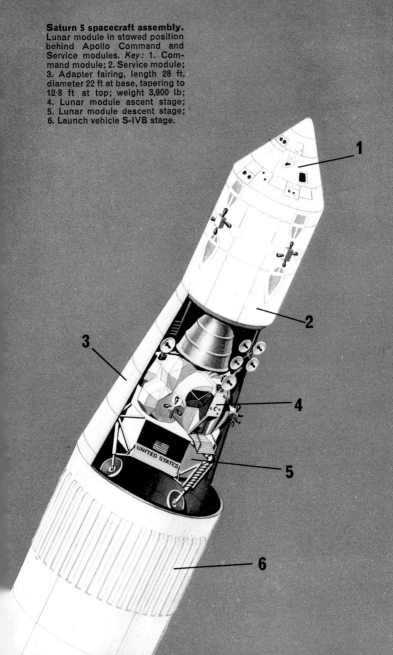

Saturn 5 spacecraft assembly.
Lunar module in stowed position
behind Apollo Command and
Service modules. *Key:* 1. Command module; 2. Service module;
3. Adapter fairing, length 28 ft,
diameter 22 ft at base, tapering to
12·8 ft at top; weight 3,900 lb;
4. Lunar module ascent stage;
5. Lunar module descent stage;
6. Launch vehicle S-IVB stage.

1

2

3

4

5

6

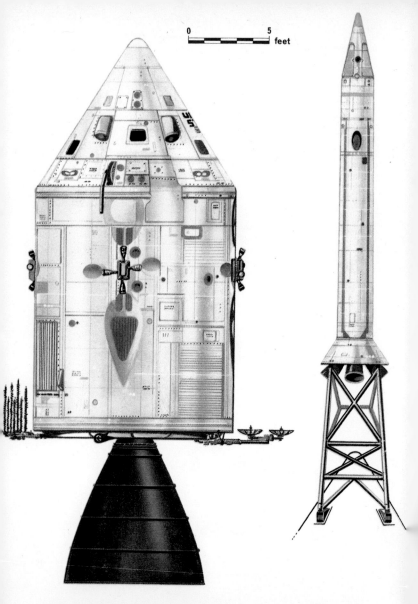

North American Apollo (Parent Craft)
Command module: Length 11·7 ft; maximum diameter over heat shield 12·8 ft;
weight 11,000 lb. Service module: Length 14 ft; diameter 12·8 ft; weight about
50,000 lb. Engine thrust 22,000 lb. Launch escape system *(right):* Length, overall
c/w tower, 33 ft 10 in.; rocket motor diameter 26 in.

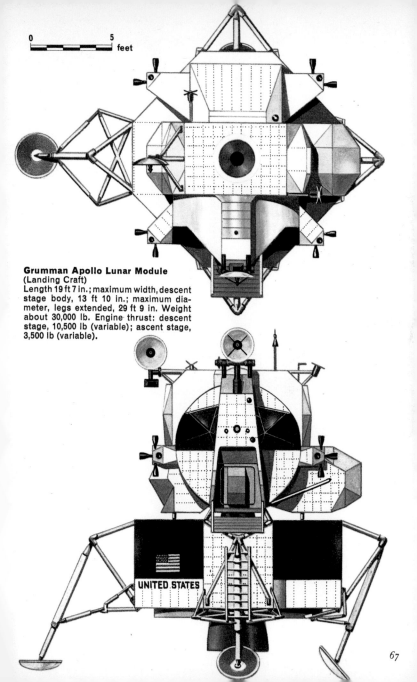

Grumman Apollo Lunar Module
(Landing Craft)
Length 19 ft 7 in.; maximum width, descent
stage body, 13 ft 10 in.; maximum diameter, legs extended, 29 ft 9 in. Weight
about 30,000 lb. Engine thrust: descent
stage, 10,500 lb (variable); ascent stage,
3,500 lb (variable).

0   5
feet

UNITED STATES

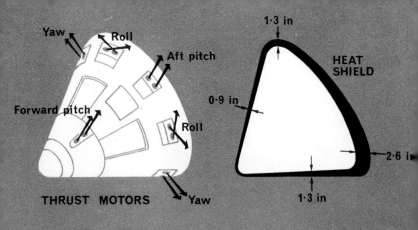

Yaw

Roll

Aft pitch

Forward pitch

Roll

THRUST MOTORS

Yaw

HEAT SHIELD

1·3 in

0·9 in

2·6 in

1·3 in

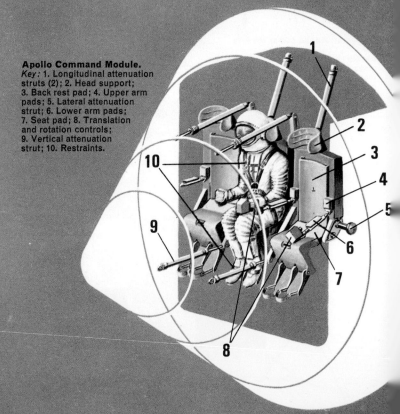

Apollo Command Module.
Key: 1. Longitudinal attenuation struts (2); 2. Head support; 3. Back rest pad; 4. Upper arm pads; 5. Lateral attenuation strut; 6. Lower arm pads; 7. Seat pad; 8. Translation and rotation controls; 9. Vertical attenuation strut; 10. Restraints.

1

2

3

4

5

6

7

8

9

10

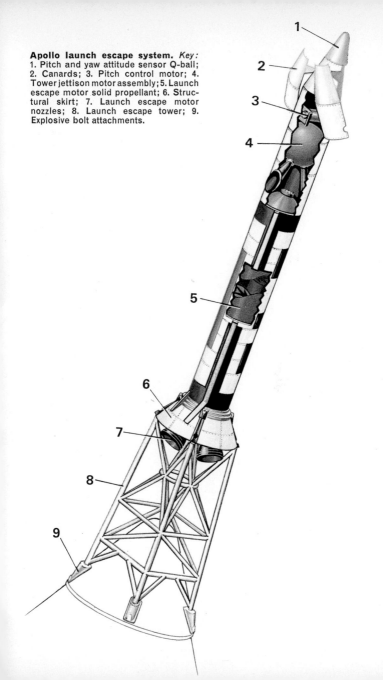

Apollo launch escape system. *Key:*
1. Pitch and yaw attitude sensor Q-ball;
2. Canards; 3. Pitch control motor; 4.
Tower jettison motor assembly; 5. Launch
escape motor solid propellant; 6. Structural skirt; 7. Launch escape motor
nozzles; 8. Launch escape tower; 9.
Explosive bolt attachments.

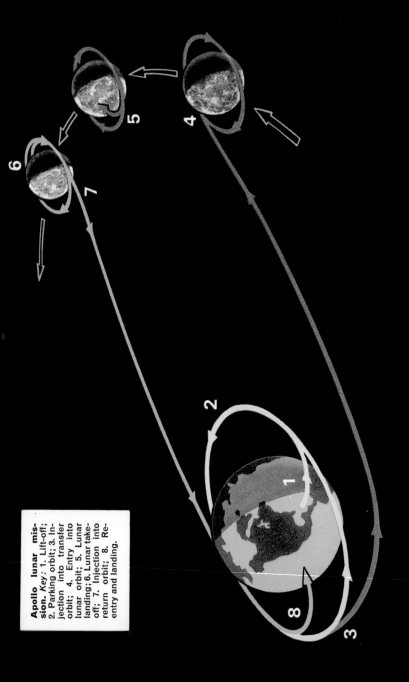

Apollo lunar mission. *Key:* 1. Lift-off; 2. Parking orbit; 3. Injection into transfer orbit; 4. Entry into lunar orbit; 5. Lunar landing; 6. Lunar takeoff; 7. Injection into return orbit; 8. Reentry and landing.

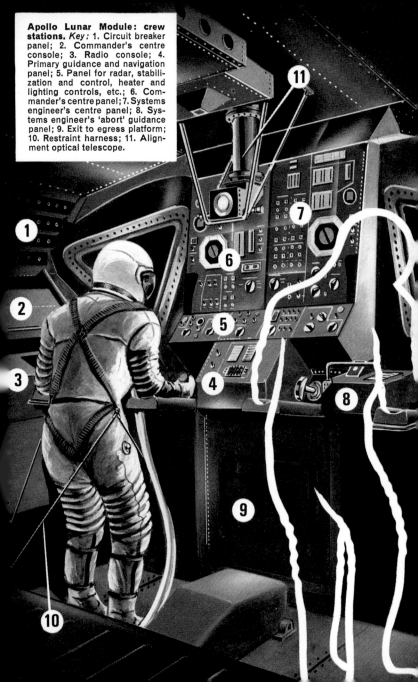

Apollo Lunar Module: crew stations. *Key:* 1. Circuit breaker panel; 2. Commander's centre console; 3. Radio console; 4. Primary guidance and navigation panel; 5. Panel for radar, stabilization and control, heater and lighting controls, etc.; 6. Commander's centre panel; 7. Systems engineer's centre panel; 8. Systems engineer's 'abort' guidance panel; 9. Exit to egress platform; 10. Restraint harness; 11. Alignment optical telescope.

(Below) Apollo lunar module descent stage (landing gear folded). *Key:* 1. Aft interstage fitting; 2. Fuel tank; 3. Engine mounting; 4. P.LSS, S-band antenna storage bay; 5. Structural skin; 6. Descent engine; 7. Insulation; 8. Thermal shield; 9. Forward interstage fitting; 10. Oxidizer tank; 11. Fuel tank; 12. Oxygen tank; 13. Helium tank/cryogenic; 14. Descent engine skirt; 15. Truss assembly (landing gear); 16. Secondary strut (landing gear); 17. Pad (landing gear); 18. Landing radar antenna; 19. Primary strut (landing gear); 20. Lock assembly (landing gear); 21. Scientific equipment bay; 22. Gimbal ring; 23. Adapter attachment point (landing gear); 24. Outrigger (landing gear); 25. Oxidizer tank; 26. Water tank.

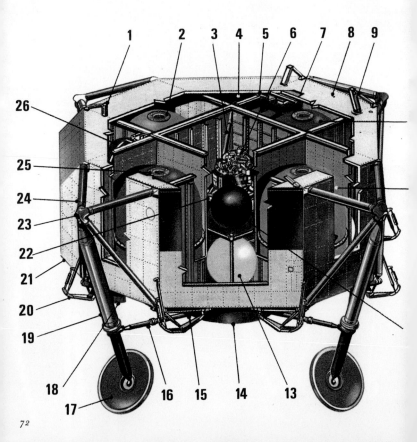

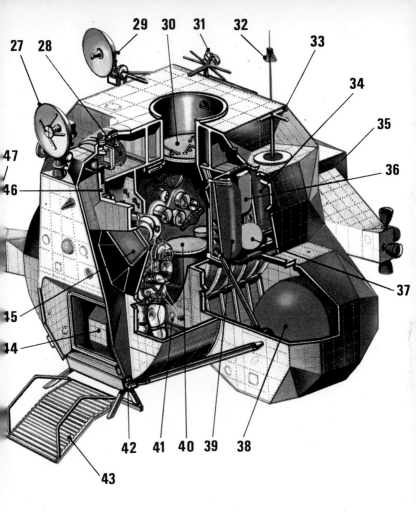

(Above) Apollo lunar module ascent stage. 27. Rendezvous radar antenna; 28. Inertial measuring unit; 29. S-band steerable antenna; 30. Docking hatch; 31. VHF antenna; 32. EVA antenna; 33. Docking target; 34. Fuel tank (RCS); 35. Aft equipment bay; 36. Helium pressure regulating module; 37. Helium tank; 38. Fuel tank; 39. Oxidizer tank (RCS); 40. Ascent engine cover; 41. Crew compartment; 42. Forward interstage fitting; 43. Egress platform; 44. Ingress/egress hatch; 45. Cabin window; 46. Alignment optical telescope; 47. RCS thruster assembly.

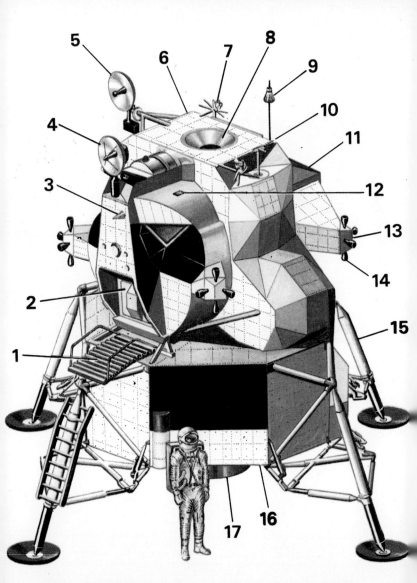

Apollo Lunar Module (complete). 1. Egress platform; 2. Ingress/egress hatch; 3. S-band inflight antenna (2); 4. Rendezvous radar antenna; 5. S-band steerable antenna; 6. Ascent stage; 7. VHF antenna (2); 8. Docking hatch; 9. EVA antenna; 10. Docking target; 11. Aft equipment bay; 12. Overhead docking window; 13. RCS thruster assembly; 14. RCS nozzle; 15. Landing gear; 16. Descent stage; 17. Descent engine skirt.

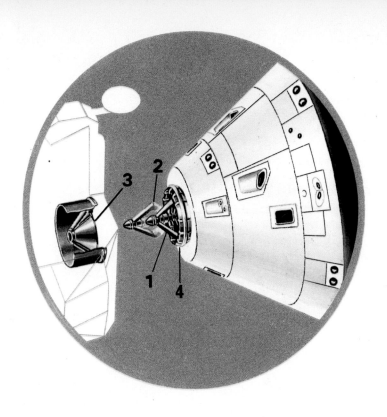

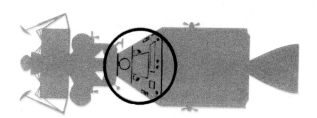

Apollo docking mechanism for linking command and service modules with lunar module following rendezvous manœuvres. *Key:* 1. Probe; 2. Probe extended; 3. Drogue; 4. Latch (12 positions).

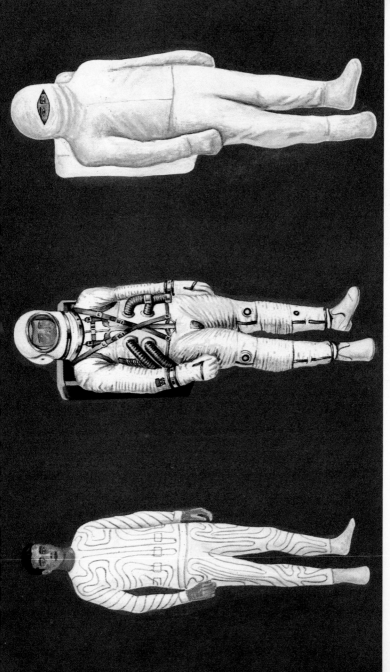

Apollo moonwear. (*Left*) water-cooled undergarment worn next to skin; (*centre*) pressure suit with portable life-support pack; and (*right*) coverall

(Top) Apollo stands ready for launching on the nose of Saturn 5; *(bottom)* first stage separates as stage two ignites 154 seconds after lift-off.

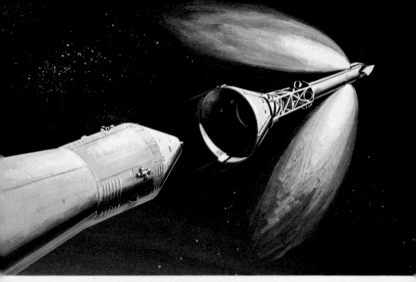

(Top) having cleared the atmosphere, escape tower and protective cone separate; *(bottom)* after delivering Apollo into a temporary parking orbit close to Earth, third stage fires again to inject vehicle into transfer orbit to the Moon.

(Top) command and service modules separate from third stage after adapter panels are blown free; *(bottom)* craft turns through 180° to line up with lunar module.

(Top) command module's docking mechanism engages docking collar of lunar module; *(bottom)* thrusters of service module pull craft free of carrier rocket's third stage.

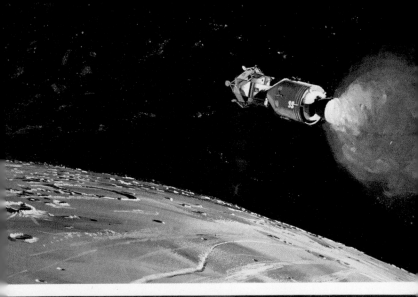

(Top) parallel with moon's surface, service module's engine fires against flight direction to put combined vehicle into lunar orbit; *(bottom)* two astronauts transfer to lunar module ready to separate craft for landing.

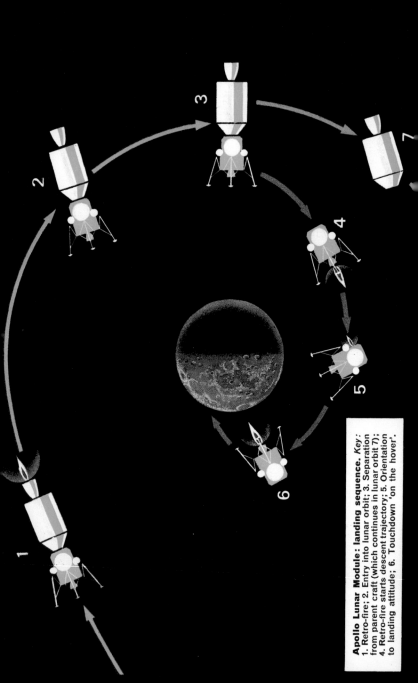

Apollo Lunar Module: landing sequence. *Key:*
1. Retro-fire; 2. Entry into lunar orbit; 3. Separation from parent craft (which continues in lunar orbit 7); 4. Retro-fire starts descent trajectory; 5. Orientation to landing attitude; 6. Touchdown 'on the hover'.

(Top) lunar module separates leaving one astronaut with parent craft in lunar orbit; *(bottom)* flare out to landing attitude with final rocket-supported hover to achieve smooth landing site.

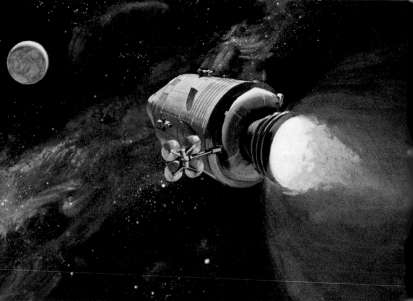

(Top) leg-supported base section of lunar module becomes launch platform for ascent stage; *(bottom)* after rendezvous and docking with parent craft, return flight begins. Lunar module is left in lunar orbit.

Apollo Lunar Module: return from Moon. *Key:* 1. Ascent module pursues phase-computed ascent path; 2. Apollo parent approaches rendezvous position; 3. Lunar module lines up for docking manœuvre; 4. Spacecraft re-connected for astronaut transfer.

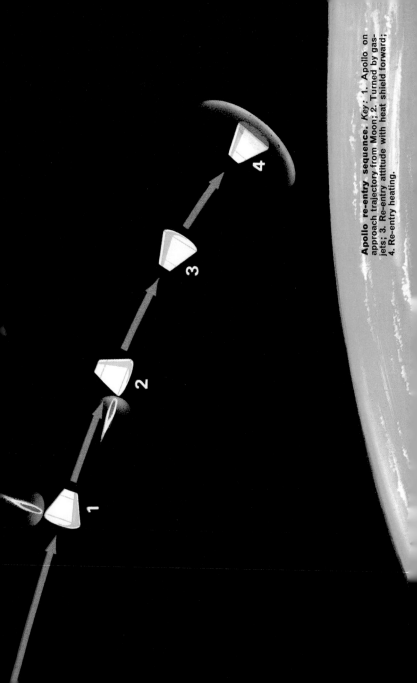

Apollo re-entry sequence. *Key:* 1. Apollo on approach trajectory from Moon; 2. Turned by gas-jets; 3. Re-entry attitude with heat shield forward; 4. Re-entry heating.

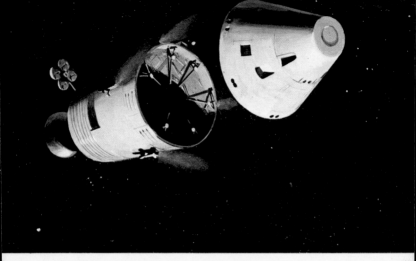

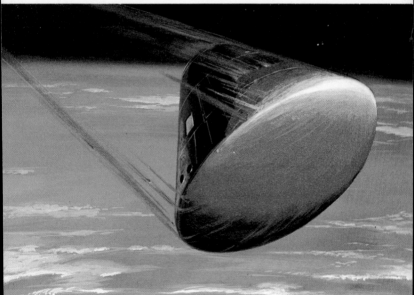

(Top) before re-entering Earth's atmosphere service module is jettisoned; *(bottom)* after command module is turned over ablative heat shield takes brunt of frictional heating.

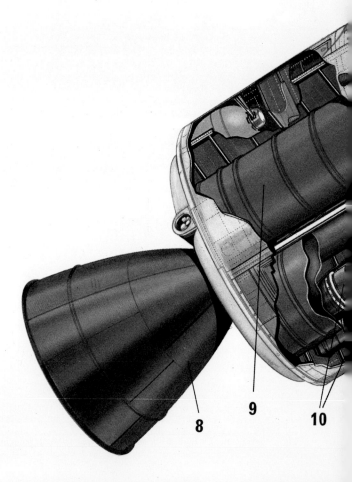

8

9

10

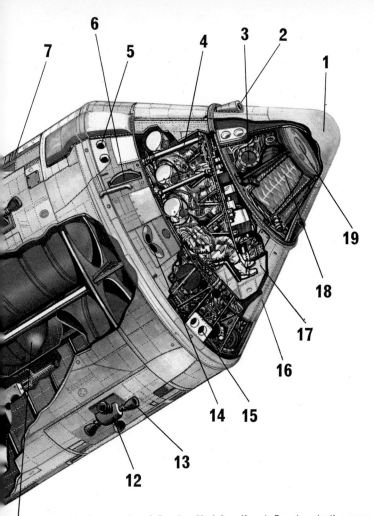

Apollo Command and Service Modules. *Key:* 1. Boost protective cover (apex section); 2. Explosive bolt attachments for launch escape tower; 3. Drogue parachutes and mortars; 4. Couch attenuation struts; 5. Pitch thrusters; 6. Antenna; 7. Environmental control system radiation core; 8. Service module propulsion engine nozzle; 9. Propellant tanks; 10. Fuel cells; 11. Helium tank; 12. Reaction control system quadrant; 13. Reaction control system engines; 14. Roll thrusters; 15. Yaw thrusters; 16. Aft boost cover; 17. Pressure cabin; 18. Parachute recovery system; and 19. Forward access tunnel.

Apollo recovery sequence.
Key: 1. Parachute housing separates; 2. Drogue parachutes deploy; 3. Landing parachutes deploy; 4. Landing parachutes reefed; 5. Landing parachutes open; 6. Capsule awaits ocean retrieval.

(Top) command module's ringsail landing parachutes fully deployed; *(bottom)* rescue helicopters close in as Apollo astronauts splash down.

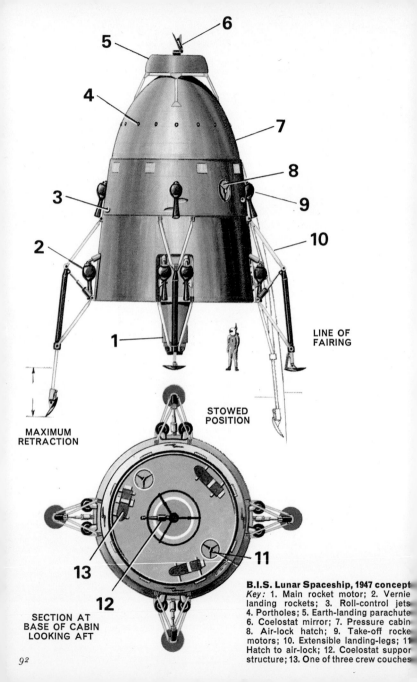

6

5

4

7

3

8

9

2

10

1

LINE OF
FAIRING

MAXIMUM
RETRACTION

STOWED
POSITION

13

12

11

SECTION AT
BASE OF CABIN
LOOKING AFT

B.I.S. Lunar Spaceship, 1947 concept
Key: 1. Main rocket motor; 2. Vernie
landing rockets; 3. Roll-control jets
4. Portholes; 5. Earth-landing parachute
6. Coelostat mirror; 7. Pressure cabin
8. Air-lock hatch; 9. Take-off rocke
motors; 10. Extensible landing-legs; 11
Hatch to air-lock; 12. Coelostat suppor
structure; 13. One of three crew couches

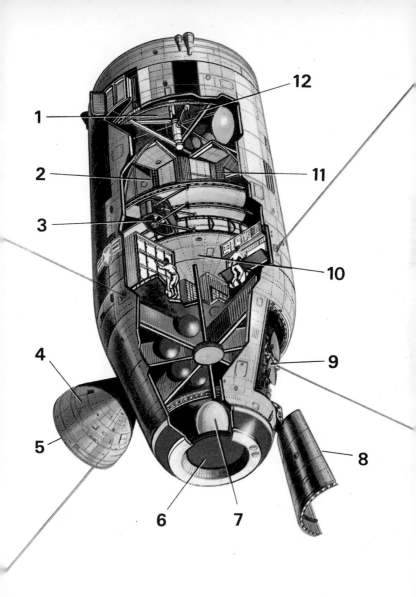

Manned Orbiting Research Laboratory (MORL); Douglas feasibility study.
Key: 1. Storage area; 2. Flight crew quarters, wardroom and galley; 3. Centrifuge; 4. Gemini-type multi-mission module; 5. Spacecraft equipment module; 6. Docking collar for Apollo-type supply craft; 7. Cargo door to experiment bay; 8. Experiment bay door; 9. Mounting pad for experiments; 10. Operations deck; 11. Hygiene facilities; 12. Power supply and life-support systems.

93

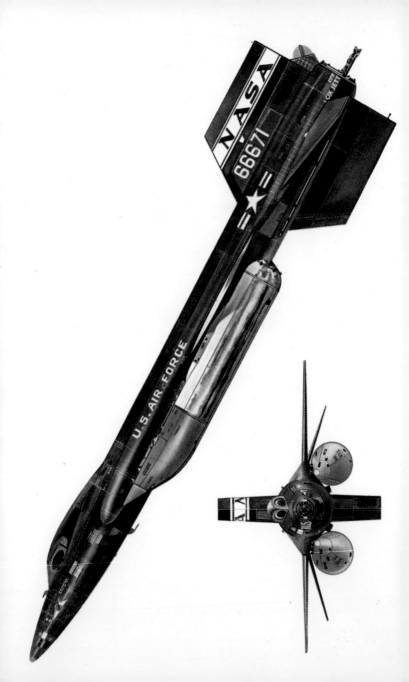

North American X-15A-2 (air-launched from B-52). Powered by: 1 × Thiokol LR-99 rocket engine. Length 52 ft 5 in.; span 22 ft 0 in.; wing area 200 sq. ft; maximum launch weight 50,914 lb; maximum landing weight 17,120 lb; maximum speed: 4,233 m.p.h. (Mach 6·33)—18 November 1966. Two external jettisonable tanks (25 ft long) with total of 13,500 lb propellants, bringing total fuel and oxidant load to 32,250 lb.

SV-5P

Length 24 ft 6 in.

Width 13 ft 8 in.

Propulsion: XLR-11
8,000 lb thrust
rocket engine

Air-launched from B-52

HL-10

Length 22 ft 2 in.

Width 15 ft 1 in.

Propulsion: XLR-11
8,000 lb thrust
rocket engine

Air-launched from B-52

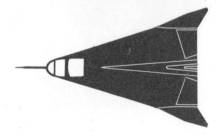

M2-F2

Length 22 ft 2 in.

Width 9 ft 7·5 in.

Propulsion: XLR-11
8,000 lb thrust
rocket engine

Air-launched from B-52

Piloted lifting-body research craft

CHAPTER ONE

RED STAR IN SPACE

The space age was barely eight hours old as our Vanguard air-liner climbed away from London Airport *en route* for Barcelona. The date was 4 October 1957, and somewhere above the Earth the world's first satellite was bleeping its radio message signifying Russia's mastery of the new technique of satellite launching. Soviet scientists working in extreme secrecy had triumphed ahead of America just forty-eight hours before the opening of an important international Space Congress, on which delegates were converging from all parts of the world.

At the time none of us knew where this object – a 23-in. sphere of polished aluminium with four long whip aerials – had been launched. However, in a triumphant communiqué, *Tass* the official Soviet news agency had announced its weight as 83·6 kg. (184 lb); incredibly, this was 163 lb heavier than the satellite which America was preparing for the forthcoming International Geophysical Year. Although a picture of the satellite, Sputnik 1, was soon to appear in the Soviet Press, there was no photograph of the actual launching or indeed any details of the multi-stage rocket responsible for its appearance in space.

As we flew on towards Spain one event of the previous few months became a talking-point among the British delegates and pressmen aboard that plane. Barely two months before, in a few guarded sentences, *Tass* had announced the launching of an intercontinental ballistic missile (ICBM). The communiqué merely stated that '. . . a super long-distance intercontinental multi-stage ballistic rocket flew at an . . . unprecedented altitude . . . and landed in the target area'. Again there were no details of the rocket, nor was it stated how far it had travelled. But clearly here was a basis for the launch vehicle of Sputnik 1 which now circled our planet every 96 min., passing over every major continent.

Next morning, after we had signed in at the conference – the

Eighth Congress of the International Astronautical Federation –
at last came the opportunity to question Soviet delegates on their
triumph.

I well recall Academician Leonid Sedov's answers to eager
questions put to him by Western delegates and correspondents
as we stood talking in a group. Was it possible that Sputnik 1
was really so massive? Had *Tass* perhaps misplaced a decimal
point? After all, America's unlaunched Vanguard satellite was
20 in. in diameter and weighed only 21 lb. Sedov's reply could
scarcely be taken seriously; he said he had been away from the
Soviet Union for a couple of weeks and therefore did not know
which satellite had been launched.

Little did we then realize that within a month another sputnik
would be in orbit with a dog-passenger, the announced weight
being 508·3 kg. (1,120·8 lb).

Throughout the whole week of the Congress in Barcelona
nothing more could be gleaned from the Russians than was contained in the original *Tass* statement, and all questions concerning the launch vehicle were met with polite but firm refusals to
comment. For ten years the Russians maintained their strict code
of silence.

As the first Russian satellites moved round the Earth in the
last weeks of 1957, so in the West equipment was quickly improvised to track them using radio, radar, and optical methods.
British observers were particularly active. Signals picked up by
the British Broadcasting Corporation's listening station at Tats-
field enabled the satellite's time of closest approach to be
estimated from signal strength and Doppler shift (analogous to
the changing pitch of a whistle from a passing train). This was
quickly supplemented by the active tracking of satellites at
Jodrell Bank. Analysis of orbital data was made by the Royal
Aircraft Establishment, Farnborough, in conjunction with many
sources including the Royal Radar Establishment, Malvern, and
the Admiralty Signals and Radar Establishment, Portsdown.

Stations in many parts of the world quickly began to gather
vital data quite unconnected with telemetry signals giving data
from instruments installed in the satellites which only Soviet

scientists could interpret. How a satellite's path was distorted (perturbed) as it circled the Earth gave a clue to the Earth's non-uniform shape or unequal mass distribution, affecting the local strength of the Earth's gravity. New information was obtained on the nature of the radio-reflecting layers of the Earth's iono-sphere by observing the scattering effect on the satellite's radio signals. The first reliable information was also obtained on the density of the upper atmosphere by observing the rate at which air drag caused the satellite to spiral ever closer to the Earth until it was burnt up by air-friction at a height of some 60 miles.

There was much to excite the scientist in those early days of satellite observation; but for the average citizen perhaps most thrilling of all was the ability to spot satellites with the naked eye as they made their transits before dawn and after dusk. Travelling at over 17,000 m.p.h. hundreds of miles up, they reflected sunlight from beyond the horizon revealing themselves to the ground observer as slow-moving 'stars' in the night sky.

Most conspicuous were the carrier rockets of Sputnik 1 and Sputnik 2. As the dog-cabin of the latter remained attached to its orbiting rocket stage, this had the greater length. Photographic and radar observations of these objects indicated lengths of 65 to 75 ft.

The last orbits of Sputnik 2 were particularly spectacular. As I watched from Coombe Hill in Surrey, it appeared to flash like a far-off beacon. This indicated that the long cylindrical vehicle was slowly turning over and over in space reflecting sunlight unevenly. The dog it contained, named Laika, had long since lost consciousness and died as its air supply gave out. Bio-medical data were received from the animal experiment for about a week after the launching when radio transmissions ceased; the dog was fed and watered from an automatic dispenser within its tiny pressure cabin but no provision was made for its recovery. Sputnik 2 remained in orbit for five and a half months. As air drag brought it closer and closer to the Earth with each successive revolution, suddenly on 14 April 1958, it was gone in a spear of flame as air-friction heated it to incandescence.

This first experiment with a living creature in orbit gave an early clue to Russia's future intentions in manned spaceflight. For America, it was a particular challenge, for the rocketry involved was obviously on a scale greater than anything then available to the Western World. This view was further reinforced in May 1958 by the launching of Sputnik 3, a cone-shaped geophysical laboratory weighing fully 1,327 kg. (2,926 lb).

Anxiety that a serious missile-gap was developing between Russia and America led to the United States broadening the scope of military surveillance of Soviet affairs.

First definitive reports of Soviet missile activity, in fact, had begun to filter through to the West by 1950 following the repatriation of certain German rocket specialists who had been rounded up at the end of the Second World War and taken to Moscow. Once in the Soviet Union they had been formed into a Collective and given facilities in a near-derelict factory in the Moscow suburb of Khimki. They were not involved in the actual design of Soviet missiles but their talents were used to help solve basic problems in such fields as propulsion, structures, and guidance. Their only contact with the Soviet rocket programme came during regular technical meetings with Soviet specialists, and the Germans could only guess at the course that Soviet rocketry was taking. Later, the propulsion group was moved to an island in Seliger Lake near the source of the Volga. It was here that an engine of 264,000 lb thrust was engineered using liquid oxygen and kerosene as propellants with a chamber pressure of 880 p.s.i.

That Stalin himself was responsible for giving the Soviet rocket programme top priority in the immediate post-war years is now part of history. The importance of developing long-range missiles had been emphasized as early as 1946 by Marshal Zhigarev, then head of the Soviet Air Force. Should there ever be an American–Soviet war, he said, the V-2 would be useless. 'What we really need are long-range rockets of great reliability capable of hitting targets on the American continent.' The trend of thought within the Kremlin at this period has been fully discussed by Dr G. A. Tokaty, formerly Chief Rocket Scientist of the Soviet Government in Germany from 1945 to 1947.* Tokaty defected to the West in

* See *Astronautics in the Sixties* by Kenneth W. Gatland, Iliffe Books Ltd.

1947. He recalls that on 14 March 1947, he was present at a meeting with G. M. Malenkov and aircraft and rocket designers. Malenkov made it clear that the existing programme of V-2 development which had been taken over from the Germans did not conform to the long-term aims of the country – 'Our strategic needs are predetermined by the fact that our potential enemy is to be found thousands of miles away. . . .'

A day later, at a meeting of the Politburo and the Council of Ministers, Stalin made the aim even clearer. 'Under Hitler, German scientists have developed many interesting ideas,' he said with great seriousness. 'This Sanger project [a scheme for a rocket-powered sub-orbital bomber] seems to represent one of them. Such a rocket could have changed the fate of the war. Do you realize the tremendous strategic importance of machines of this kind? . . . The problem of developing transatlantic rockets is of extreme importance to us.'

This was the turning-point in Soviet ambitions. At this meeting Stalin personally suggested, and the Council of Ministers readily agreed, that a special State Commission should be established with the responsibility for managing the development of long-range rockets. Its initial members were: Colonel-General I. A. Serov (First Deputy Minister of the NKVD and Chairman); Professor Colonel G. A. Tokaty-Tokaev (Chief Rocket Scientist and Deputy Chairman, from the Soviet Air Force); Professor M. V. Keldysh (from the Ministry of Armaments); Professor M. A. Kishkin (from the Ministry of Aircraft Production), and Major-General Vassily I. Stalin (Marshal Stalin's son).

Meanwhile, the first task of the German Collective had been to assist in the launching of reconstructed German V-2s from a site which had been hastily improvised on the steppes of Kazakhstan, some 125 miles east of Stalingrad (now Volgograd). The first of these $12\frac{1}{2}$-ton rockets, fired on 30 October 1947, travelled a distance of 185 miles and landed in the target area. A second launching on 13 November was much less successful. A guidance fault caused the rocket to oscillate wildly when it reached 500 ft, the fins were torn off and it plunged to destruction within sight of the launch crew.

On the evidence of Dr Tokaty, much-improved rockets of Soviet manufacture but retaining certain features of the V-2 were being produced in quantity in 1949–50. They were 'built under Soviet administrators, by Soviet workers, from Soviet materials, on Soviet soil' and bore the name Pobeda (Victory). Whereas the original German V-2 had a range of 190 miles, Pobedas could reach up to 560 miles. Examples first appeared in the Red Square military parade of November 1957 and in the West they are known by the NATO code-name Shyster.

According to Dr Tokaty, the first Rocket Divisions of the Soviet Armed Forces, equipped with V-2s and Pobedas, were formed in 1950–1. Upper-air research with rockets of the V-2 type started in the autumn of 1947; from 1949 it was continued with Pobedas.

Systematic research into the effects of spaceflight on living organisms began in 1949. From 1949 until 1952 dogs were rocketed to heights of some 60 miles, chiefly to test the effects of weightlessness. They travelled inside a pressure cabin installed in the nose-cone of Pobeda rockets which separated in flight and was parachute-recovered.

As more and more Intelligence reports filtered through to the West of Soviet activity at this site, steps were taken by the United States to set up radar stations on the perimeter of Soviet territory to monitor rocket activity which had begun to increase in the early 1950s north of the Caspian. By 1955 the US Air Force had put into operation a large fixed-beam radar at Diyarbakir, a mountain village in Turkey, which looked out across the Black Sea to the region in the Soviet Union where these experiments were in progress. The area is now famous as Kapustin Yar (literally Cabbage Crag), the Soviet cosmodrome from which early Cosmos satellites were launched into orbits inclined at 49° to the Equator.

However, long before the first Cosmos vehicle left this base in March 1962, missile testing had gone on almost continuously since the first V-2 launchings. In conjunction with other US radar stations on the perimeter of the Soviet Union, a disturbing picture of Russia's growing capability with long-range rockets was being built up by the mid 1950s.

Not only was it possible to spot missiles under test as they appeared above the radar horizon, but radio tracking was possible by homing on to the telemetry signals which carried data from various instruments embodied in the missiles. The electronic surveillance network gave information on the rockets' direction, speed, and altitude and it was possible to predict their impact points with considerable accuracy. The data showed that by the mid 1950s the Soviet Union was firing medium-range ballistic missiles, some of which impacted in the Kyzyl Kum Desert to the south-east of Kapustin Yar.

Meanwhile, the bigger rocket that Stalin insisted must be capable of reaching America, a weapon designed to carry a thermonuclear warhead that was both crude and heavy, was fast being developed by Soviet engineers.

The Americans had been faced with similar problems and as early as 1951 Convair (now General Dynamics) designed a massive rocket for purposes of H-bomb delivery, having nearly the same capability as the first-generation Soviet ICBM. In fact, had a Pentagon missile investigation committee not recommended cancellation of the project in 1953, on the grounds that the vehicle exceeded engineering experience, America could have matched Soviet early gains in space achievement. The proposed 200-ton multi-stage rocket had a first-stage thrust of 875,000 lb obtainable from a cluster of seven engines.

However, in military terms, abandonment of the big rocket was a wise decision. Towards the end of 1953 US physicists reported to the President the feasibility of a dry 'lightweight' thermonuclear warhead and a breakthrough in missile size was at hand.

Even so potential carriers were still heavier than the Atlas ICBM that eventually emerged. Convair in 1954 actually built a mock-up of a 650,000-lb thrust rocket designed round a cluster of five engines; it stood 90 ft tall and was 12 ft in diameter. When the operational SM-65 Atlas-D finally appeared, there were two 150,000-lb thrust engines in the jettisonable boost section and a central sustainer of 65,000-lb thrust. Lift-off weight was 255,000 lb.

The race to develop the hydrogen bomb led to Russia exploding her prototype device on 12 August 1953. Radiation sampling indicated the bomb was 'dry' though undoubtedly still unwieldy for missile installation. Although the Americans had exploded a thermonuclear device in the Pacific on 1 November 1952, it was 'as big as a house' and meant only for experimental purposes. It was not until 1954 that the Americans succeeded in testing a 'dry' H-bomb.

By then it must be presumed that the Soviet Union was well on the way with the task of marrying the H-bomb to a multi-stage rocket capable of launching it over thousands of miles. Thus, the Russians acquired an ICBM, cumbersome by American standards, but which could lift far heavier payloads than Atlas. Its use as a space booster was soon to be demonstrated.

It was in the mid 1950s that reports of another large cosmo-drome under construction east of the Aral Sea began to reach the ears of Western Intelligence. This information helped to spur the development of another surveillance device, the celebrated U-2 reconnaissance aircraft.

Developed in great secrecy by Lockheed Aircraft Corporation, the U-2 was first used for high-altitude reconnaissance over the Soviet Union as early as the summer of 1956. Ostensibly it was used to gather weather information and this became a convenient 'cover story' for any infringement of Soviet airspace.

It has been reported that a U-2 spotted the first Soviet ICBM on its launch pad at the Baikonur/Tyuratam complex in August 1957, but as all information obtained by the Central Intelligence Agency (CIA) is secret, even today it is impossible to confirm the whole truth behind these early penetrations of the Iron Cur-tain. Before missiles were launched on test from this new site at target areas in the Central Pacific, they were directed towards the Kamchatka Peninsula in the Soviet far east.

However, the cat was fully out of the bag on May Day 1960 when Lieutenant Francis Gary Powers made his famous recon-naissance flight over the Soviet Union. We now know that on that day, as world leaders were gathering for a Summit Con-ference, a large multi-stage rocket was being prepared at the Baikonur cosmodrome. The U-2 flew at great height across the Afghan frontier on a course that took it over Stalinabad (now

Dushambe), south of Tashkent, and on across Aralsk and Baikonur. High above the Soviet cosmodrome its cameras looked down on the launch pads, blockhouses, and administrative buildings of Russia's most secret installations.

On flew the U-2 to the Chelyatinsk area and the approaches to Sverdlovsk where allegedly it was brought down by a Soviet surface-to-air missile (NATO code-name Guideline).

Fourteen days later the world knew what the CIA had long suspected; Russia was beginning a series of space experiments designed to put a man into orbit. According to *Tass*, the vehicle, known as Spacecraft 1, circled the Earth every 91·1 min. at a height ranging between 229 and 188 miles. It weighed 10,008 lb and contained a 'dummy cosmonaut'.

In the circumstances it was fortunate that this first test-vehicle did not contain a human being for when the capsule was commanded to re-enter the Earth's atmosphere it must have been wrongly orientated; instead of the retro-rocket reducing its speed it drove it into a higher orbit. Several parts of this vehicle were subsequently tracked as they circled the Earth, and in fact it was more than five years before the cabin section and its cosmonaut dummy re-entered the atmosphere on 15 October 1965.

What seems to have been a sub-orbital test for this spacecraft occurred in January 1960 when Russia began a series of test-firings of multi-stage launch vehicles impacting in the Central Pacific. Development of a 'nose-cone' which apparently remained intact after travelling 7,760 miles and reaching a maximum height of some 700 miles and a maximum speed of 16,150 m.p.h., not only suggested that Russia had solved the re-entry problem for ballistic missiles but that substantial progress had been made towards producing a re-entry vehicle for manned spaceflight.

After the initial firing on 20 January, Professor Boris Konstantinov, Director of the Physical and Technical Institute of the USSR Academy of Sciences, reported: 'Firstly, the discrepancy between the target and the point where the nose-cone, simulating the last stage of the rocket, hit the water represents only 1/6,000th part of the total range. Secondly, the two-way radio communication was maintained throughout the trajectory, including transit through the dense layers of the atmosphere over the target area. Thirdly, the thermal shield of the nose-cone fully protected it from destruction while it was moving at immense speed in the lower layers of the atmosphere. And lastly, a heavy satellite can carry a device making possible a safe descent through the whole atmosphere to the point of landing.'

Since that time Russia has used target areas in the Central Pacific for many different rocket tests. These launchings have been followed closely by the US Air Force and Navy who use radar and other sensors to monitor the ballistic re-entry bodies as they re-enter from space and approach their Pacific targets. Sometimes the last stage of Soviet rockets ascend 800 miles into space with a test-vehicle that separates in flight. The Americans, operating mainly from Hawaii, Kwajalein Atoll, and Johnston Island find the tests particularly useful for their own radar practice for the 'interception' of missile targets, Kwajalein Atoll and adjacent islands being the test centre for US Nike-Zeus and Sprint anti-missile missiles.

American ships and aircraft work together in these assignments monitoring the activities of Soviet tracking ships on station on the perimeter of target areas. When the re-entry body actually strikes the sea, the impact is recorded by sonar-devices giving precise measurements. After one particularly extensive series of firings between 13 September and 28 October 1961 the Soviet commander of tracking ships complained: 'US ships and aircraft do not leave the Soviet tracking ships alone for a single moment. American planes daily "buzz" the ships, coming closely over the mastheads and US ships manœuvre in such a way that they interfere with our work. Nevertheless, we quietly get on with our business.'

In the newspaper *Red Star* the unidentified commander claimed that the rockets landed accurately in the predetermined area after travelling some 7,500 miles. 'We worked calmly in the target area,' he said. 'We made contact with the rockets precisely at the appointed time and carried out measurements without any fear that they might deviate from their courses.' Accuracy was confirmed 'by very accurate measuring instruments in our ships'.

Following the mishap to the first Soviet spacecraft and its dummy cosmonaut, four more launchings were to take place before it was considered safe to entrust a man to orbital flight. The first of these occurred on 19 August 1960, when a 10,140-lb craft began orbiting the Earth with the dogs Strelka and Belka as passengers. Also in the cabin were smaller animals, insects, and plants.

The dogs occupied a pressurized container attached to the chassis of the ejection seat. The flight lasted just over a day and was entirely successful. Correctly orientated at a backward inclined angle for retro-rocket firing on the seventeenth orbit, the re-entry capsule separated from the instrument module as planned; after penetrating the atmosphere the dog-container was successfully ejected on the seat chassis for parachute recovery. Thus, the mission was a complete rehearsal for the subsequent Vostok manned missions.

After the flight the Russians released their first guarded statement on the vehicle. It included the information that the re-entry capsule travelled nearly 7,000 miles from the moment of being ejected from orbit to the time it had dropped to about 23,000 ft. It was subjected to a maximum deceleration of some 10 g.

A hatch on the capsule was released by barometric relays at a height of 23,000 to 26,000 ft whereupon the dog-container was ejected. It landed at a speed of 20 to 26 ft/sec.

At the time it was explained that this was an emergency procedure used on this occasion to test the escape system before manned spaceflights were attempted. Later, when human cosmonauts were being sent into orbit, its use was described as optional. In fact, it became standard practice for Vostok cosmonauts to eject in this way rather than remain in the re-entry capsule.

In the case of Spacecraft 2, it was stressed that the animals would have been safely recovered had they remained inside the capsule which came down near by. The landing, stated to have been only $6\frac{1}{4}$ miles from the preselected target point, was exceptionally accurate. An error of only 3 ft/sec. in velocity would have deflected the capsule over 30 miles. An error of about 300 ft in estimating the spacecraft's height over the Earth would have meant a deflection of nearly 3 miles, and an error of 1 min. of an arc in attitude a deviation of 30 to 40 miles.

First details of the spacecraft which was to become Vostok were also given, though at the time care was taken not to reveal any hint of its configuration. On the exterior were control jets and the 'orientation system's reserve high-pressure gas containers'. There were also 'the transducers of the scientific apparatus, the radio aerials, and experimental solar batteries. A system of heat insulation prevented the ship from burning up during the descent through the atmosphere. In the walls of the cabin were heat-resistant portholes and quickly detachable pressurized hatches.'

Apart from command signals from ground stations, the vehicle 'was guided automatically by means of a high-precision orbit control system'. Chemical and solar batteries powered the space-craft's instruments. Solar batteries 'were placed on two half-discs 1 metre in diameter'. They remained locked on the Sun regardless of the spacecraft's attitude or position.

After the retro-rocket had started the vehicle on its descent path, the instrument module was separated and allowed to burn up in the atmosphere. This contained telemetry equipment; part of the scientific payload for studying cosmic rays and shortwave radiation from the Sun; equipment associated with guidance in orbit; heat-regulation apparatus and the retro-rocket system. Jettisoning of the instrument module greatly reduced the vehicle's mass, thereby 'reducing the demands on braking and recovery devices'. Exactly what these devices were was not disclosed but, as it turned out, they were simply a heat shield and parachutes.

One must acknowledge, however, the care with which Soviet engineers and scientists approached the problem of manned spaceflight. Years after the Strelka and Belka mission, it was revealed that their craft carried pieces of human skin which had been volunteered by doctors to determine the effects of radiation in space. The donors were Dr Kapichnikov, Dr Rybakov, and Dr Novikov of the Moscow Institute of Experimental Biology. Small flaps of skin, cut from their shoulders and thighs, were

placed in sterilized glass bottles with a nutritive solution and dis-
patched to the cosmodrome. Similar control samples of skin were
kept in the laboratory.

After spending a day in orbit, the flaps of skin were returned
to the laboratory on 22 August 1960, where they were implanted
together with the control samples back on the donors. It was
found that the skin samples which had been in space began to
knit on the eighth day, later than the control specimens which
had remained in the laboratory. Nevertheless, together with the
other bio-medical information that was being accumulated, it
was good confirmation that a man could endure a day in orbit
without harmful results.

Yet within four months the Soviet space programme was to
receive another setback. On 1 December 1960, two more dogs
Pchelka and Mushka, were launched in the 10,221-lb Spacecraft
3. The orbit achieved was lower than on the previous occasion,
but the main fault appeared to have been the attitude of the spacecraft at the time of retro-fire. Having spent a day in orbit like
the previous vehicle, it was delivered into an incorrect re-entry
trajectory and the two dogs plunged to a fiery death as their
capsule burnt up like a meteor.

How this affected the course of the Soviet space programme
was never revealed. But it is probably significant that the next
experiment on 9 March 1961 was limited to a single orbit. Only
one dog Chernushka travelled in the 10,360-lb spacecraft and
the orbit achieved was still closer to the Earth. Yet the tempo was
building up. Just sixteen days later another launch vehicle left
the Baikonur cosmodrome to orbit a 10,350-lb spacecraft with
the dog Zvesdochka. Successfully recovered after 1 orbit, this
was the final qualification test for the craft which carried Yuri
Gagarin.

As the historic day of the world's first human spaceflight drew
nearer the rigid secrecy that had prevailed in the Soviet Union
showed signs of breaking down. It began with a rumour from
Moscow that a Russian cosmonaut had been launched in secret
on Friday, 7 April. A BUP message to London at midnight on
11 April quoted unidentified sources as suggesting that the

cosmonaut was still undergoing physical examination by Soviet
scientists, but that he was suffering from post-flight effects of a
nature more emotional than physical. BUP continued:

> It is reported that the astronaut was a professional test pilot
> and son of a prominent aircraft designer. Russian and
> foreign journalists are maintaining a round-the-clock vigil,
> waiting for an official announcement. However, official
> sources still maintained an absolute silence, neither denying
> nor confirming the reports. Moscow Radio went off the air
> just before midnight without mentioning a spaceflight.

The story was further embellished from the Soviet Union by a
French correspondent who suggested that the mystery cosmonaut was none other than Lieutenant-Colonel Vladimir Ilyushin,
son of the famous Soviet aircraft designer. In fact there was no
truth in these rumours. Mr Pierre Salinger, then Press Secretary
to the White House, said that the US Government had no information whatsoever of a Soviet space launching on the day
concerned. As for the young Ilyushin, he was traced to a Chinese
health resort in Hangchow where he had arrived some time before. Having received a bad leg injury in a road accident the
previous June, he had left the Moscow Traumatology Hospital
and remained bedridden at home until the end of January 1961.
He was still walking with a stick.

The world did not have long to wait for the real story. On the
morning of 12 April 1961, at 0759 hr. BST (0959 hr., local
Russian time) came the big announcement:

> The world's first spaceship, Vostok [East], with a man on
> board was launched into orbit from the Soviet Union on
> 12 April 1961. The pilot space-navigator of the satellite-
> spaceship Vostok is a citizen of the USSR, Flight Major
> Yuri Gagarin.
>   The launching of the multi-stage space rocket was suc-
> cessful and, after attaining the first escape velocity and the
> separation of the last stage of the carrier rocket, the spaceship
> went into free flight on a round-the-Earth orbit. According to

the preliminary data*, the period of revolution of the satellite-spacecraft round the Earth is 89·1 min. The minimum distance from the Earth at perigee is 175 km. (108·7 miles) and the maximum at apogee is 302 km. (187·6 miles), and the angle of inclination of the orbit plane to the Equator is 65°4'. The spacecraft with the navigator weighs 4,725 kg (10,418·6 lb), excluding the weight of the final stage of the carrier rocket.

Lift-off occurred at about 0907 hr. local time (0707 hr. BST) from the Baikonur cosmodrome, and 1 complete orbit was accomplished – matching the performance of the two previous dog-flights. The flight lasted 108 min., re-entry being initiated at 1025 hr. local time when the craft was over Africa. The landing was made 30 min. later near the village of Smelovaka in the Ternov District, near Saratov. Gagarin remained in the re-entry capsule which came to earth by parachute. The total distance travelled was 25,400 miles.

Much was made of the fact that Gagarin was an ordinary citizen of the Soviet Union. Born on 9 March 1934, the son of a collective farmer in the Gzhatsk District of Smolensk, he entered a secondary school in 1941. His studies were interrupted by the German invasion.

After the Second World War the Gagarin family moved to Gzhatsk, where the young Yuri's studies resumed in secondary school. In 1951, he graduated with honours from a vocational school in the town of Lyubersy, near Moscow. He received a foundryman's certificate, at the same time completing a course at an evening school. Yuri then studied at an industrial technical school in Saratov, on the Volga, from which he graduated, also with honours, in 1955.

It was while attending the industrial school that the man who was to become the world's first cosmonaut took his first steps in aviation. He attended the Saratov Aero Club where he completed a course of training in 1955, to enter the Air Force School

* These figures were subsequently revised by the Soviet authorities, as follows: perigee 112·4 miles; apogee 203 miles; period 89·1 min., and inclination 64°57'.

at Orenburg. Graduating with a first-class certificate two years later, he became a pilot in the Soviet Air Force. Following his acceptance for training as a cosmonaut he joined the Communist Party of the USSR in 1960. Married, his wife Valentia is one year his junior. At the time of the flight their two daughters Yelena and Galya were two years and one month old respectively.

Gagarin's impressions of the flight were later given in an interview with *Tass*. He said the sunlit side of the Earth was plainly visible; one could easily distinguish the shores and continents, islands and rivers, large areas of water and folds in the land. Over the Soviet Union he clearly saw 'the big squares of collective farms, and it was possible to distinguish ploughed land from meadows'. Prior to going into orbit, he had never flown above 15,000 metres (49,213 ft). From orbit he was able to discern the Earth's spherical shape. He described the sight as 'quite unique and very beautiful'. One could appreciate

> the remarkable colourful change from the light surface of the Earth to the completely black sky in which one can see the stars. The dividing line is very thin, like a belt of film surrounding the Earth's sphere. It has a delicate blue colour. And this transition from the blue to the dark is very gradual and lovely. It is difficult to put into words.

When he emerged from the Earth's shadow, Gagarin said the horizon looked different. 'There was a bright orange strip along it, which again passed into a blue hue and once again into dense black. What struck me most remarkably was how near the Earth seemed, even from a height of 187 miles.'

He did not see the Moon. The Sun was 'tens of times brighter than on Earth', the stars were bright and distinct, with far more contrast than when seen from the Earth.

Of his reactions to weightlessness, Gagarin said he felt excellent. Everything was easier to perform. 'This was understandable. Legs and arms weigh nothing. Objects were swimming in the cabin, and I did not sit in the seat as before but was suspended in mid-air. During the state of weightlessness I ate and drank.'

Gagarin recalled that he worked normally, noting his reactions in a log-book. 'Handwriting did not change, though the hand was weightless. But it is necessary to hold the writing-block or it would float away from the hands.' He maintained radio contact on various channels.

He reported his conviction that weightlessness had no effect on the ability to work. Transition from weightlessness to normal gravitational forces happened smoothly. 'I ceased to be suspended over the seat but eased myself into it.'

During a visit to Paris I was able to question Gagarin on various aspects of his pioneer mission. He confirmed that he remained in the capsule instead of ejecting from it for separate parachute recovery. The spherical capsule, he said, was orientated into the correct re-entry attitude for drag-braking by having its mass off-centre; he felt no ill-effects either during orbital flight or when re-entering the Earth's atmosphere.

At the Twenty-sixth Salon International de l'Aéronautique et de l'Espace in 1965, I examined with Gagarin a full-size Vostok re-entry capsule which seemed complete in every detail. The forward face of the sphere was charred and scored and I inquired if this was, in fact, one of the capsules which had been into space. After some difficulty with the interpreter he admitted the exhibit was only a realistic representation which had been heated to simulate the appearance after re-entry.

As Gagarin had been given a new appointment in 1963 un-connected with the cosmonaut training centre, I asked if he now looked upon himself more as an administrator than a cosmonaut. Unhesitatingly, he said he expected to go into space again, not once but several times.

A young Russian engineer by the name of Sergei played a part in testing the Vostok cabin before Gagarin's first flight. During simulation tests at a Soviet space centre he was sealed in the capsule as technicians at control consoles produced conditions that might arise during an actual spaceflight. One of the enforced emergency situations Sergei faced was large variations of cabin temperature. After a test, he said his clothes 'were dripping wet' and he lost over 13 lb in weight.

Vostok comprised two main components. The *spherical capsule* complete with cosmonaut's ejection seat, life-support equipment, and parachute landing system. This was attached to a *combined equipment module and retro-rocket*, which also contained instruments used during orbital flight. The equipment is described in detail in Chapter Four, but essentially it comprised the following:

1 Instruments and equipment necessary for maintaining human functions, including an air-conditioning system, a pressure-control system, food and water, and means for removing the body's waste products;
2 Flight-control equipment and manual controls;
3 Landing system;
4 Radio equipment for communicating with Earth;
5 A system for automatically recording the work of the instruments, radio telemetry system, and various sensors;
6 A television system for observing the cosmonaut at ground stations;
7 Instruments for recording physiological reactions of the cosmonaut;
8 Retro-rocket;
9 Orientation system;
10 Flight-control system;
11 Radio system for measuring orbital parameters;
12 Temperature-control system, and
13 Electrical supplies.

A summary of the flight of Vostok 1 follows:

12 April 1961
Moscow time (hr.)   *Event*

0907	Multi-stage rocket lifts-off at Baikonur cosmodrome.
0951	Automatic orientation system switched on. After emerging from Earth's shadow, solar sensor locks on the Sun and orientates Vostok 1 on to it.

0952	Vostok 1 passes over Cape Horn, moving north-east. Gagarin radios he is well and equipment working normally.
1015	Automatic programming unit commands sequence for switching on retro-rocket; Vostok 1 approaching Africa.
1025	Retro-rocket fired to begin descent trajectory.
1035	Vostok 1 re-entry capsule – now separate from instrument/retro-rocket module – enters dense layers of Earth's atmosphere.
1055	Capsule lands in predetermined area.

With Gagarin's pioneer orbit successfully completed, confidence grew in the ability to keep a man in space for a day, as the Russians had done the previous August with the dogs Strelka and Belka. On 6 August 1961 at 0900 hr. Moscow time, another Russian citizen – Major Gherman Titov – lifted off in Vostok 2. While the flight was in progress, *Tass* gave the aims as 'research into the effects upon the human organism of a prolonged orbital flight to study man's working capacity during a sustained state of weightlessness'. According to preliminary data,* the communiqué continued, 'the spacecraft has been put into an orbit close to the calculated one, with the following orbital parameters: perigee 178 km. (110 miles), apogee 257 km. (159 miles), inclination to Equator 64°56′, and initial period 88·6 min. The spacecraft weighs 4,731 kg. (10,432 lb), excluding the final stage of the carrier rocket.'

The communiqué continued: 'Two-way radio communication is being maintained with Major Titov. The cosmonaut is transmitting on frequencies of 15,765, 20,006, and 143·625 Mc/s. A Signal transmitter also on board operates on a frequency of 19·995 Mc/s.

As the flight progressed frequent communiqués were broadcast by Moscow Radio. The cosmonaut was observed by television

* These figures were subsequently revised by the Soviet authorities as follows: perigee 114 miles, apogee 152 miles, period 88·46 min., inclination 64°5′36″.

to be operating his instruments normally, while a constant stream of bio-medical information on his condition was recorded at ground stations. During the third orbit he consumed his first meal in space, a three-course lunch in paste form squeezed from tubes. After resting for an hour during the fourth orbit, he conducted physical exercises and further work-tasks according to the pre-arranged flight plan. For an hour Titov 'tested Vostok's manual controls', reporting on the good behaviour of the vehicle when orientated by this method.

On the sixth orbit Titov exchanged greetings with Yuri Gagarin at the Command Centre and again swung the craft round its centre of mass using manual controls.

From 1830 hr. (Moscow time) to 0200 hr. the following day, the cosmonaut was scheduled to sleep. He reported: 'Before turning in I first fixed my hands, which seemed to be suspended in the air, and fell into a light slumber.' At first he slept fitfully and then fell into a deeper sleep, 'without dreams'. In contrast to sleeping on Earth he felt no necessity to turn from side to side. So good was Titov's sleep that it lasted 35 min. longer than envisaged in the programme, which gave rise to some anxiety at the Soviet Command Centre, all radio transmissions having been suspended during this period.

With Titov back in contact with ground stations, the cosmonaut breakfasted and resumed his work apparently unperturbed by the effects of weightlessness, making observations of the Earth and performing various scientific and engineering tasks. It was some time after the mission that Soviet scientists disclosed that bio-medical problems were not entirely absent. 'Under weightlessness,' Professor Vladimir Yazdovsky reported, 'unpleasant sensations of a vestibular character were felt with increasing strength, especially when the cosmonaut turned his head sharply or was observing swiftly moving objects.' These sensations diminished after Titov's sleeping period but did not wholly disappear until he encountered decelerative forces during re-entry. Professor Yazdovsky emphasized, however, that some people might be more sensitive to weightlessness than others.

Unlike Gagarin, Titov ejected from the Vostok 2 capsule to

make a separate descent by parachute. He told a Moscow Press Conference: 'After the retro-rocket fired and the craft entered its descent trajectory, I felt very fit and decided to try the second landing system. At low altitude the seat was ejected and my further descent was made by parachute. The ship landed successfully near by.' Titov completed 17 orbits of the Earth in 25 hr. 18 min., making his return in the Saratov area some 450 miles south-east of Moscow. During the flight he had travelled 703,150 km. (436,656 miles). Aircraft and helicopters were in the air to watch the return from orbit and to pick up the cosmonaut after he had landed.

It was a year and five days before the next Soviet manned spacecraft stood ready on its launch pad at the Baikonur cosmodrome. Lift-off of Vostok 3 came at 1130 hr. (Moscow time) on 11 August 1962; but the first announcement gave no clue to the key experiment that was being planned. The objectives were given as further information on human reactions to spaceflight, study of the cosmonaut's working ability under weightlessness, scientific observations, and 'the further perfection of systems of cosmic ships, and methods of their communication, guidance, and landing'.

No hint was given of feverish activities then proceeding at the cosmodrome in a bid to launch a second spacecraft into proximity with the first on the following day.

Vostok 3 carried Major Andrian Nikolayev in a launching said to have gone with clockwork precision. The orbit had the following initial parameters: perigee 111·8 miles, apogee 145·3 miles, period 88·3 min., and inclination 64°59′. Western observers watched the flight continue into the second day and then came the announcement over Moscow Radio that Vostok 4 had been launched with cosmonaut Lieutenant-Colonel Pavel Popovich. According to *Tass* launching had been effected 'from the same launch complex' of the cosmodrome as Vostok 3. Moreover, launching had been made 'within 1 second of the scheduled time'. The timing was vital for the object was to produce a separation of only 5 km. (3·1 miles) between the two ships at the point where Vostok 4 was injected into orbit.

Post-flight analysis of orbital data showed that the closest distance achieved was actually about 6·5 km. (4 miles). However, as the craft had no provision for matching orbits by rocket thrust, they rapidly drifted apart. At the start of the thirty-third orbit the separation distance was 850 km. (528 miles) and at the beginning of the sixty-fourth, 2,850 km. (1,770 miles). The orbit of Vostok 4 was remarkably similar to that of its companion. Figures for the initial orbit were quoted as perigee 111·8 miles, apogee 157·7 miles, period 88·5 min., and inclination 65°.

A wide range of experiments was performed during the group flight. The Russians reported obtaining an enormous amount of observational data, photographs, log-book records, and telemetry recordings. Communications were maintained with the two spacecraft by ground stations, and between the two cosmonauts in orbit. The men were required to get in touch with each other every half-hour, calling in turn. For the first time television broadcasts from spacecraft were transmitted to many countries. Since the flights lasted 4 and 3 days respectively, much of the data received had to do with bio-medical effects.

The cosmonauts had to conduct regular psychological, physiological, and vestibular tests. These involved keeping a careful watch on pulse, respiration frequency, appetite, adaptability to noise, vibration, overstrain, and weightlessness; also the ability to work and sleep.

Conditions within both spacecraft were stated to have remained within the following parameters: cabin pressure 755–775 mm.; oxygen percentage 21–25; carbon dioxide percentage 0·5 max., and temperature 13–26°C, the higher values representing conditions before lift-off.

Bio-medical measurements telemetered to Earth were:

a Electrocardiograms of heart condition and circulatory system;
b Pneumograms of breathing;
c Electroencephalograms reflecting conditions of central nervous system, also permitting analysis of sleep and alertness, fatigue and excitation;

d Skin-galvanic reactions by ohmic resistance of the skin to assist study of central nervous system; and

e Electro-oculogram, recording movements of the eyes to give objective information concerning vestibular disorders; in conjunction with pulse and breathing frequency, etc.

In the case of (*e*) tiny silver electrodes, placed at the outer corners of the cosmonauts' eyes, recorded bio-currents of the muscles of the eye-ball. Eye movements to left or right were recorded respectively as positive and negative currents. Skin-galvanic reflexes (*d*) were registered by measuring skin resistance by electrodes placed on the front and lower third of the cosmo-naut's right shin. Changes occurred in the electrical potential of the skin and skin resistance as a result of various vegetative and emotional stimuli.

Pulse and respiration rates are given in the table below:

	Vostok 3 Nikolayev (*min.*)	*Vostok 4* Popovich (*min.*)
Pulse frequency 4 hr. before lift-off	72	80
Breathing frequency 4 hr. before lift-off	11	15
Pulse 1 hr. before lift-off	88	100
Pulse 5 min. before lift-off	115	110
Pulse during acceleration to orbit	120	130
Pulse during orbital flight	50–80	50–80
Pulse before re-entry	96–104	85
Breathing frequency before re-entry	11	16

It was also necessary to assess how convenient was the use of the sanitary equipment. The cosmonauts were also expected to assess hygienic conditions in the cabin, including air purity, temperature, humidity, and lighting. The men were also expected to assess the method of taking food and evaluate the food's quality. Meals – more varied than before – were taken four times a day, first breakfast at 0500–0600 hr. (Moscow time), then a second breakfast at 0800–0900 hr., dinner at 1400–1500 hr., and supper at 2000–2100 hr. As well as the tube-packed foods, there were meat cutlets, roast veal, fillet of chicken, pastries, special sweets, miniature loaves, sausages, dragees, and chocolate.

Experiments included floating freely in the cabin while unrestrained by the seat harness. Nikolayev reported spending four periods totalling three and a half hours in this condition and Popovich three periods totalling about three hours. They had to determine how much personal orientation was possible; also what was the most convenient posture to adopt when the muscles were relaxed.

Although at first it was claimed that the cosmonauts experienced no adverse effects of their prolonged exposure to weightlessness, at the 1964 Cospar Symposium it was revealed that post-flight disturbances affecting cardiovascular response persisted for 7–10 days. Professor Vassily Parin, Director of the Institute of Normal and Pathological Physiology of the USSR Academy of Medical Sciences, reported reactions mostly concerned with the heart and blood-vessels. However, he said the central nervous system and metabolism were also affected.

An interesting experiment performed under weightlessness by Popovich concerned the observation of air bubbles in an hermetically sealed flask about two-thirds full of water. When undisturbed, the cosmonaut reported, all the air gathered in the middle of the flask and the water remained round the walls. After the flask was shaken the large bubble split into a multitude of smaller bubbles which gradually merged again into one big bubble. Popovich said he also sprayed water inside the cabin. The water formed small globules which slowly gravitated to the walls settling on them.

Both cosmonauts described the beauty of the Earth as it passed beneath them. They could easily pick out coastlines, rivers, mountains, and towns; they observed 'sunrises and sunsets', and while over North America they watched thunderstorms in the atmosphere miles below. At the time of the flight the Moon was full and when the craft was in the Earth's shadow the surface appeared 'as a great blanket' against which the cosmonauts could discern the lights of towns.

Yuri Gagarin was on duty at the operations centre near Karaganda with Titov and other cosmonauts. He explained that his task was to maintain direct contact with Nikolayev and Popovich during the countdown and boost periods. He spoke to the men in orbit several times during the 4 days of the operation.

The double landing must have placed a particular load on the ground-control and recovery teams. The flight programme called for landing in Kazakhstan at a latitude of 48°N using an automatic system. First into position was Vostok 3 whose retro-rocket fired at 0924 hr. (Moscow time) on 15 August. Ejecting from the capsule at low altitude Nikolayev parachuted down at 0952 hr. in an area south of Karaganda 48°02′N, 75°45′E. The capsule landed undamaged near by.

Nikolayev's flight was 94 hr. 22 min., during which he completed 64 orbits of the Earth and covered a total distance of 2,639,600 km. (1,639,190 miles).

The retro-rocket of Vostok 4 fired at 0930 hr. (Moscow time); Popovich ejected in the lower atmosphere and touched down south of Karaganda at 48°10′N, 71°51′E. Again the capsule was stated to be undamaged. Flight time was 70 hr. 57 min.; total distance covered, exceeding 48 orbits, was 1,981,050 km. (1,230,230 miles).

With the first Vostok group flight safely completed, it looked obvious that the Soviet space programme was being directed towards the perfection of orbital rendezvous techniques. This view was strengthened by a speech which Yuri Gagarin gave at the Paris Congress of the International Astronautical Federation in September 1963. He said techniques being worked out in his country involved the assembly and refuelling of spacecraft in orbit. When I saw Gagarin again in 1965 I reminded him of this statement, asking if the Soviet programme was more concerned with a space-station or a Moon-flight. He replied that sending men to the Moon and assembling a space-station were part of the same problem.

The second Soviet group flight strengthened the Western view that orbital rendezvous was Russia's primary objective. Vostok 5 left the Baikonur cosmodrome on 14 June 1963, at 1459 hr. (Moscow time), entering an orbit inclined at 65° to the Equator, ranging between 112·5 and 146 miles with an initial period of 88·4 min. It carried cosmonaut Lieutenant-Colonel Valery Bykovsky on a flight which lasted 5 days. Bykovsky conducted a series of tests similar to those of his predecessors. Several times he orientated the ship in flight using manual controls; performed various medical tests; observed the Earth, the horizon, the Moon, and the stars; operated the craft's equipment; maintained radio communications with the ground, and floated freely in the cabin.

While the TV camera was operating he demonstrated his new freedom to viewers on Earth. 'I floated up to the portholes of the spacecraft and carried out observations of the ground,' he later explained. 'It is extremely peculiar. The slightest push sends you flying in the opposite direction and, with your eyes closed, you cannot tell what your position actually is.' Apart from the conventional exercises performed by earlier cosmonauts, he did 'power exercises with a rubber strip' which helped to maintain his physical capability to work under weightlessness. He also ate, rested, and slept. He ate four times every 24 hr.; food was the 'ordinary terrestrial kind' and his appetite 'excellent'. He slept well.

Bykovsky said he could easily distinguish rivers, lakes, and oceans. Water in the seas and oceans was of different colours. He described the curvature of the horizon, noting the 'beautiful range of colours, with reddish hues predominating'. On the ground 'roads and towns were visible, towns being particularly clear at night'.

There were amusing moments too. While transmitting a routine report which mentioned 'I had a motion of the bowels', owing to interference ground control received the word as 'stuk' (knocking) instead of 'stul' (bowel motion).

There was uproar in ground control, Bykovsky said: 'I was bombarded with questions. They wanted to know what had gone wrong with the craft. What kind of knocking had I heard? Was it a buzzing or banging? I hurriedly explained that I had merely made use of my sanitary appliance.' In reply, he heard loud laughter: 'My colleagues on the ground were reassured and normal work was resumed.'

Whether or not it had been envisaged that Vostok 6, with the woman cosmonaut Valentina Tereshkova, would be launched the next day to follow the pattern of the first group flight has not been explained. Western observers believe there was a 'technical hold' at the Baikonur cosmodrome which prevented lift-off when Vostok 5 passed overhead on the seventeenth orbit, delaying the launch for another 24 hr. Miss Tereshkova eventually lifted away from the cosmodrome within her Vostok 6 capsule at 1230 hr. (Moscow time) on 16 June. The ship's initial orbit closely matched that of Bykovsky's. Angled at 65° to the Equator, it ranged from 114 to 145 miles with a period of 88·3 min.

Soon after Valentina went into orbit the two craft 'closely passed each other'. The two cosmonauts held their first conversation at about 1300 hr. At 1400 hr. Moscow Television broadcast the first live pictures from Vostok 6. They showed Miss Tereshkova, clad in her spacesuit and helmet, speaking confidently by radio to ground control. She appeared calm and smiling and reported she felt well. By 2200 hr. Vostok 5 was completing its thirty-eighth orbit and Vostok 6 its seventh.

The distance between the two spacecraft varied throughout the flight, from 5 km. (3·1 miles) to several hundred kilometres. Nevertheless, communication between them remained steady.

Telemetered medical data and visual television observations showed that both Bykovsky and Tereshkova were standing up well to orbital flight.

Afterwards the woman cosmonaut gave her reactions at a Moscow Press Conference.

> The flight tasks included work with various equipment in the cabin, the life-support system, and radio communications. I recorded observations in a log-book, on tape and on ciné-film. I endured well the state of weightlessness and quickly adjusted to it. Certainly, it was rather odd to sleep with one's hands hanging in mid-air, but I remembered Gherman Titov's experience and put my hands into my harness while I slept.

I did not dream. After sleeping I performed physical exercises. I enjoyed my meals. I had a varied diet. True, towards the end I began to want some black bread, potatoes, and onions.

The woman cosmonaut continued:

I am often asked how I was able to train myself for such an unusual and unfeminine task as piloting a spacecraft. Some people think there is nothing complicated in this, that the automatic equipment aboard the craft functions by itself and that the role of the woman cosmonaut is insignificant. However, a passive role did not suit us. We understood that our role was an active one, most important being manual orientation of the ship and adjustment of the life-support system.

My girl friends and I decided to prepare for the real thing in full measure. This meant determined study, hard work and daily and varied training.

Whereas all the previous cosmonauts had been Air Force jet-pilots, Valentina was a civilian. She was given the title of Junior Lieutenant. Apart from the obvious value of comparing male and female reactions to spaceflight, she was basically a test of any fit and adequately prepared person to go into space. Her background was that of a textile worker who took up parachute jumping as a sport.

Born in a village near Yaroslavl on 6 March 1937, her father was a tractor-driver on a collective farm; he was killed in action in the early days of the Second World War. Valentina started school in Yaroslavl in 1945, when her mother moved there to work at the textile mills.

Valentina herself began work at the age of sixteen, at the Yaroslavl tyre factory, but continued her studies at night school. In 1955 she transferred to the Krasnyi Perekop (Red Canal) textile mill, and at the same time undertook a correspondence course at a technical school. It was largely on her initiative that a parachute-jumping section was set up by the local aero club, and she took part in this sport with great enthusiasm.

After being accepted for training as a cosmonaut in 1962 she learnt to fly various aircraft. It was only then that she began to learn how to control a Vostok. 'I am convinced,' she said, 'that spacecraft leaving for long voyages to other planets will be piloted by our engineers, designers, workers – and textile workers like me.'

Part of the women cosmonauts' training involved flights in a specially adapted Tu-104 transport aircraft. Flown along powered parabolic trajectories this allowed the weightless condition of spaceflight to be simulated for about 30 sec., when the trainees could experiment by floating freely inside the specially padded cabin. Here they learned how to work various equipment under conditions similar to that of orbital flight.

Parachute training was also continued. 'We jumped again and again in different conditions,' Valentina said. 'This gave us a great deal of experience and prepared our morale for the achievement of complex spaceflights.'

She explained how the women worked hard to become familiar with every part of the spacecraft. This was followed by persistent training in the control and operation of the craft.

> It was part of my assignment to guide the craft manually. I switched on the manual control system, noted and recorded gas-pressure of the orientation system and set the stop-watch. The position of the Earth in the porthole was such that it was necessary to orientate the craft in pitch. After this I quickly followed with roll and yaw orientation. I stopped the stop-watch, then observed and recorded the instrument readings. I was glad to see how little fuel I had used. The spacecraft handled well and proved easy to control.

Radio communication during the flight provided much reassurance. 'When Valery and I were talking to each other on short-wave, I had the impression we were sitting in the same room. It seemed the radio waves I was receiving gave me new energy which increased my strength and raised my spirits.'

Valentina said she felt this particularly during her conversations with Mr Khrushchev. 'Yes, Nikita Sergeyevich Khrushchev has become a real radio operator; we followed all the radio communication rules in our conversation. We used the call signals and ended by saying "over".'

The whole flight was full of unforgettable impressions, such as the frequent sunrises and sunsets, and the rapid change in the nature of the terrain below – continents, oceans, seas, clouds, rivers, mountains, towns, and fields.

When she received instructions to return on the third day, all systems worked perfectly; the retro-rocket fired and by the increased g-loading she realized that the capsule had entered the dense layers of the atmosphere. Flames blazed outside the porthole.

As time spent in space increased, so extra safeguards were taken to ensure the continued safety of the cosmonauts. In the case of Valentina Tereshkova and Valery Bykovsky, for example, close observation of activity on the Sun was made before the flight. Professor Anatoli Blagonravov said astronomical observatories were enlisted for these studies. With the help of geophysical rockets a vertical section of the upper atmosphere was studied, which made it possible to obtain, directly, samples of the level of radiation at a given moment. Of the spacecraft, Blagonravov noted that 'substantial improvements were made to the life-support system, providing greater comforts for the cosmonauts'. Whereas previous flights had concentrated on the human organism, it had been possible to include a number of scientific experiments in Vostoks 5 and 6. These included observations of constellations, photography of the Sun and the Earth's disc at sunrise and sunset, as well as observations of the Earth's surface.

Professor Vladimir Yazdovsky, the medical authority, explained that preparations to send a woman into space required special research 'because of the different anatomical and physiological characteristics'. A new system was devised for recording the respiration and cardiac activity, for example, and there were special pre-flight experiments concerning the effects of acceleration and deceleration on the female organism.

Physiological information was telemetered to Earth, but the pulse count was also sent by a special channel of the craft's

Signal transmitter which operated continuously for tracking purposes. Use was made of techniques for studying electrical phenomena of the heart, brain, eyes, and skin, and also seismo-cardiography.

Radiation monitoring during the flight was effected by physical and biological dosimeters. Bykovsky's total radiation dose was 35–40 millirads, and Tereshkova's 25 millirads. Both cosmonauts experienced a certain rise in the heart rate before landing. Bykovsky's pulse rate in orbit varied between 46 and 80 per min. and respiration between 12 and 22 per min. Tereshkova's pulse ranged from 58 to 84 per min. Yazdovsky reported that 'consider-able fluctuations in the frequency of heart-beats occurred within short intervals of time'; respiration rate ranged between 16 and 22.

According to Soviet officials, Tereshkova's flight was planned to last 24 hr. However, as her condition remained satisfactory it was decided to allow her mission to continue for 3 days. Yaz-dovsky explained that 'her sleep during the flight removed the emotional stress and restored the ability to work'. Her pioneer mission, in fact, lasted 71 hr. during which 48 orbits were com-pleted. The total distance covered was 1,970,990 km. (1,224,084 miles).

The return to Earth was made on 19 June at 1120 hr. (Moscow time) some 390 miles north-east of Karaganda on latitude 53°.

Having passed the period of maximum heating, with speed reduced to 493 m.p.h., the hatch cover was automatically fired off at an altitude of 22,966 ft. Valentina ejected in the seat at 21,385 ft. Twenty seconds later, at 13,123 ft altitude, the capsule landing parachute was triggered by the automatic descent con-trol. Valentina herself was still high in the air, swinging lazily beneath her parachute, as her capsule bumped down.

Bykovsky was down 2¾ hr. later, having completed no fewer than 81 orbits of the Earth in a flight lasting over 119 hr.; the total distance covered was 3,325,957 km. (2,065,420 miles). Hav-ing ejected from the Vostok capsule he landed at 1406 hr. (Moscow time) some 337 miles north-west of Karaganda, also on latitude 53°.

Although in common with some of her cosmonaut brothers Valentina Tereshkova experienced certain post-flight disturbances in blood-pressure, body chemistry, and nervous responses as determined by measurement of brain rhythms, these effects were stated to have disappeared within 15 days.

A few months after her flight it was announced that Valentina was to marry cosmonaut Andrian Nikolayev. The wedding took place on 3 November 1963.

The following February it was my privilege to meet the remarkable woman whose courageous exploit had thrilled the world. It is the custom of the British Interplanetary Society to make awards for significant 'firsts' in astronautical achievement. Yuri Gagarin received the Society's first gold medallion when he visited London in 1961 and Valentina (now Mrs Nikolayeva-Tereshkova) came specially at the Society's invitation on 5 February 1964.

With other representatives of the Society I was at London Airport to greet the lady following her arrival by Tu-104. One could not fail to be impressed by her modest and gentle manner, and the confident way in which she dealt with questions from the Press. Certainly there were no signs of physical or psychological lassitude; in fact, quite the reverse. Although she was pregnant and her baby had obvious interest for Soviet scientists, there was no special cosseting on that account. She attended all the functions of her strenuous seven-day programme. One evening, though clearly feeling the strain, she stood with the Soviet Ambassador and his wife for nearly three hours welcoming guests at two mammoth Embassy receptions given in her honour.

Naturally, Valentina was proud of her unique achievement. But after receiving the award from Dr L. R. Shepherd, the BIS President, at a special meeting of the Society, she spoke of the 'workers, engineers, technicians, scientists, and all Soviet people' who had made her flight possible. She also acknowledged the large and friendly family of Soviet cosmonauts which contained 'a number of women who are to perform in future many cosmic flights'; she stressed the desire to preserve outer space for peaceful scientific purposes.

Although we were no wiser after her visit about technical features of the Vostok programme, there were many interesting conversations. When I inquired after her husband,* who had been forced by pressure of work to remain in Moscow, Valentina told me he was busy with exams at the Zhukovsky Air Force Engineering Academy. She herself expected to resume her studies after the birth of her baby.

Of her own spaceflight I was interested to know exactly what she had been able to see of the Earth's surface. At the time there was heated debate in America over the detail observations reported by Gordon Cooper from his Mercury capsule. He had described seeing roads, buildings, and smoke from chimneys. Certain experts in visual acuity were frankly incredulous and there was talk of Cooper having suffered hallucinations.

When I put the problem to Valentina she was sceptical of the ability to resolve such fine detail from orbit; but later American observations were to prove the correctness of Cooper's assertions (see page 158).

In the minds of Soviet specialists there had never been any question that Valentina would not have a perfectly healthy baby, though naturally she received special medical care. Just twelve months after she had looked down on the Earth from space, calmly reporting her reactions to scientists on the ground, her baby – a 6 lb 13 oz girl – was born. For some reason news of the birth at the Moscow Gynaecological Institute on 8 June 1964 – reportedly by Caesarian section – was delayed for 48 hr.; but probably this was to allow time for a thorough medical check.

Writing in the March 1966 issue of *Aviatsiya i Kosmonavtika* about her life and future plans, Valentina said she was not only continuing her cosmonaut training but also studying at the Zhukovsky Academy. She was also running her home and looking after her family at the 'Stellar Village' near Moscow where the Soviet men and women cosmonauts receive their training. She denied stories that her daughter, Yelena, had abnormality as a result of her spaceflight.

* Nikolayev replaced Yuri Gagarin as commander of the cosmonaut group in April 1965, being made up to the rank of Colonel.

It should be recalled, too, that there has been one other famous space-mother, the bitch Strelka (Little Arrow) which orbited the Earth 17 times in an unmanned Vostok. Five months after her return to Earth, Strelka had six bright-eyed playful puppies. One, called Pushinka (Fluff), was given by Mr Khrushchev to Mrs Jacqueline Kennedy.

It was at the wedding of Andrian Nikolayev and Valentina Tereshkova in November 1963, that astute Western correspondents noticed among the guests two pioneers of Soviet astronautics. One was Academician Valentin P. Glushko, a fifty-five-year-old combustion engineer who worked on liquid-propellant rocket engines in the 1930s. The other was Sergei P. Korolev, fifty-seven, also prominent in the 1930s in structural aspects of rocket engineering. The connexion seemed to confirm these men as prominent in the development of Vostok and its multi-stage launcher. Korolev had previously been identified in a photograph taken at the Baikonur cosmodrome on the morning of Gagarin's flight.

According to Dr G. A. Tokaty, the former Soviet rocket specialist, in 1945 Korolev 'was made responsible for the further development of the German V-2. Later his group designed an ICBM, the successful launching of which was announced on 27 August 1957.' He later became 'one of the chief designers of the Sputnik and Vostok capsule-carrying rockets'.

Korolev's part in the development of Soviet space technology was confirmed shortly after he died on 14 January 1966, when the Soviet Press published an obituary, part of which is reproduced below. It was signed by Leonid Brezhnev, Alexei Kosygin, Nikolai Podgorny, and other Soviet leaders, and also by Academicians Mstislav Keldysh, Mikhail Millionshchikov, Anatoli Blagonravov, and Leonid Sedov.

Academician Sergei Pavlovich Korolev, a prominent Soviet scientist, a member of the Presidium of the USSR Academy of Sciences, a Communist, twice Hero of Socialist Labour, and a Lenin Prize-winner, died in Moscow on 14 January at the age of fifty-nine. In Sergei Korolev our country and world science have lost an outstanding scientist in the fields of rocketry and space research, and a distinguished constructor of the first artificial space satellites, which ushered in the era of man's exploration of outer space.

Sergei Pavlovich Korolev was born in the town of Zhitomir on 30 December 1906, the son of a teacher. According to the *Tass* news agency he started work in the aircraft industry in 1927. Three years later he graduated from the Aero-mechanics Department of the Bauman Higher Technical School, having studied without interrupting his work, and in the same year he completed his studies at the Moscow School of Aviation.

After becoming acquainted with Konstantin Tsiolkovsky and with his ideas, Korolev took up space rocket engineering and became one of its founders. In 1933 he helped to form a group for the purpose of studying rocket flight and this group designed the first experimental rockets. From that time until the end of his life he devoted all his energies to the development of Soviet space rocket engineering.

Sergei Korolev was a prominent designer of space-rocket systems which were used for launching the first artificial Earth satellites, for carrying the Soviet pennant to the Moon, for a flight round the Moon, and for photographing the side of the Moon which is not seen from the Earth, the news agency reported.

Piloted spacecraft in which man travelled for the first time into outer space and stepped out into space, were designed under Korolev's direction. Sergei Korolev trained large numbers of scientists and engineers who are now working in many space-rocket engineering research institutes and design bureaux.

Korolev lived long enough to see two more Soviet manned spacecraft go into orbit. These were the two Voskhod (Sunrise) vehicles.

As Gagarin had forecast and the flight of Valentina Tereshkova made credible, Voskhod 1 was the first attempt to orbit non-pilot crew-members capable of performing specialist duties. With the late Colonel Vladimir Komarov were a doctor, Boris Yegorov and a scientist, Konstantin Feoktistov.

Yegorov's experience was particularly important as it allowed medical experience to be applied, for the first time, directly to conditions as they existed in orbit.

The first Voskhod entered an orbit, inclined at 64°54' to the Equator, ranging between 100 and 255 miles from the surface.

Few details of the 5,320-kg. (11,731-lb) spacecraft were given following the launching which occurred at 7 hr. 30 min. 1 sec. on 12 October 1964. Such photographs as were officially released suggested similar external dimensions to the Vostok. The launch vehicle was clearly an uprated version of the standard multi-stage rocket. The re-entry capsule had been re-designed to provide accommodation for three men seated side-by-side; apparently the centre position was slightly forward. Although Gagarin later told me that Voskhod was an entirely new design, it clearly owed much to existing Soviet components and techniques.

However, there were no ejection seats and the crew dispensed with pressure suits. A pressure of 1·1 atmospheres was maintained in the cabin. The men wore silver-grey woollen suits with blue jackets and white helmets with headphones. Pressure suits for emergency use were stowed in a locker. New systems incorporated in the vehicle included two sets of retro-rockets, main and reserve, allowing the ship to enter a higher orbit with greater margins of safety. Television cameras permitted 'transmission not only from the cabin but also of the ship's environment', and an attitude control system included 'ion-plotters of the direction of the ship's velocity vector'. This was taken to mean a system of small ion-engines used as a back-up for the conventional gas-jet orientation system, purely for test purposes.

The ship had two ultra-short-wave and short-wave radio-telephone channels, one telegraph system, and a radio receiver operating on short and medium wavebands. There were also 'innovations' in the method of direction finding.

During the flight Konstantin Feoktistov described luminous particles which at times could be observed outside the portholes. He thought they could be dust particles from the body of the ship. The crew gauged the particles' distance against the antenna;

it proved to be about 3 ft. In space such particles could be expected to travel with the craft but, Feoktistov remarked, 'we
observed a slow relative movement'. They were between 5 and
50 microns in size and like terrestrial dust particles, 'they shone
in the sunlight and were visible for a few dozen seconds'.

As the cosmonauts aboard Voskhod 1 had no means of ejecting
from the re-entry capsule, they had to remain inside for the
touchdown. This occurred some 312 km. (194 miles) north-east
of Kustanai in Kazakhstan. The landing parachute opened at
16,000 ft when the speed was about 720 ft/sec. In order to soften
the touchdown the vehicle had a system of braking rockets which
ignited just before the capsule, hanging beneath its parachute,
made contact with the ground. Sixteen orbits were completed in
a 415,936-mile flight lasting 24 hr. 17 min. 3 sec. The capsule
'was intact and could be used again'.

Yet another milestone in space history was reached at 1000 hr.
(Moscow time) on 18 March 1965, when Voskhod 2 lifted off
from the Baikonur cosmodrome. Inside were two men, Colonel
Pavel Belyaev and Lieutenant-Colonel Alexei Leonov.

Orbiting between 107 and 308 miles above the Earth, at the
standard 65° inclination, they travelled higher than anyone had
gone before. The mission had one major and dramatic objective:
to allow the spacesuited Leonov to emerge from the craft in orbit
by means of an airlock.

Records of the mission submitted to the International Aeronautical Federation in Paris stated that Leonov spent a total of
23 min. 41 sec. outside the cabin. Total weight of Voskhod 2,
without the rocket's final stage, was 12,529 lb, total distance
travelled 445,420 miles, and the flight duration 26 hr. 02 min.
17 sec.

Television pictures of Leonov leaving the ship suggested that
the spacecraft was a 'stretched' version of the Vostok. This was
later confirmed by photographs of the nose-cone of the launch
vehicle in a preparation building.

Leonov was seen emerging from a hatch opening at the end of
an airlock which appeared to come from the side of the space
capsule. Side-by-side seating enabled him to leave the cabin

from the left side, the airlock itself apparently being inflatable. Once the cosmonaut was inside, the cabin hatch was closed while Leonov, secure in his suit, waited for air to be pumped from the airlock chamber. When vacuum-equivalent conditions were obtained, the outer airlock doors were opened and he climbed out in space. Without the airlock, it would have been necessary to depressurize the entire cabin before egress as indeed was done in the case of the American Gemini spacecraft.

Few details were forthcoming on the design of the extra-vehicular pressure suit. A Soviet medical specialist, Vladimir Krichagin, described it as 'a miniature hermetic cabin which consists of a metal helmet with a transparent visor, a multi-layer hermetic suit, gloves, and specially designed footwear'. The suit had its own power circuitry feeding communications, and an arrangement of sensors giving data on physiological functions.

Internal air pressure, Krichagin said, had to be at least 0·4 atmosphere. Even then the suit inflated considerably and it was tiring to work inside without articulated joints.

Before going into space, nitrogen had to be eliminated from the cosmonaut's organism; prolonged respiration in pure oxygen literally washes nitrogen out of the tissues of the body and then the pressure can be safely reduced. In space there must be a steady supply of pure oxygen for the cosmonaut. It should be borne in mind that his body too, has to 'breathe'; every hour a human being gives off up to 300 kilo-calories of heat to the surrounding media. Left uncontrolled the cosmonaut's body temperature would therefore rise and he could suffer heat-stroke. Hence Leonov's spacesuit had a special air-conditioning system through which air circulated at room temperature; this air carried away excess heat of the body and moisture exuded from the skin.

To protect the cosmonaut from solar heat and from cold in the shadow of the Earth or the spacecraft, the suit was covered by a strong layer of thermal insulation and coloured white. Air for ventilation and oxygen for respiration, Krichagin said, could be taken from the spacecraft's supply or from cylinders mounted on the cosmonaut's back. The air used was rejected into the environment.

Leonov emerged from the airlock as the spacecraft entered its second orbit. When I saw him at the Space Congress in Athens in 1965, he confirmed that he had remained outside for about 10 min.; another 10 min. was spent inside the airlock – a total of 20 min. in vacuum. He had been connected with the spacecraft by a lifeline which included 'a telephone cable and telemetric wires'. No oxygen reached him through the tether; he was dependent entirely on the life-support pack on his back. Leonov regulated his own suit pressure. There were two settings. Before he left the cabin it was 0·27 atmosphere; when he stepped out into space it was 0·4 atmosphere and he reset it to 0·2¼ before climbing back. Belyaev wore a similar extra-vehicular suit.

Leonov fixed a television camera to a bracket on the edge of the open airlock before climbing out. There was a second camera outside the ship. The externally mounted cameras showed Leonov launching himself gently into space and performing gyrations at a distance of some 15 ft. His easy movements about his centre of mass and the way he was able to control his tumbling action by arm motions gave added confidence that man would be able to work effectively in space if necessary on the outside of his spacecraft.

Of the future, Academician M. V. Keldysh said: 'Use of an airlock instead of cabin depressurization would allow groups of cosmonauts to emerge from a ship in orbit and transfer from one craft to another.'

Yet still this flight did not demonstrate the ability of Voskhod to manœuvre from one orbit to another, essential for perfection of the technique of orbital rendezvous. However, at a Moscow Press Conference, Keldysh remarked that manœuvres were possible with this craft similar to those performed with earlier, unmanned, Polyöt sputniks. It could have remained in space for a month.

Despite the apparent success of the Leonov experiment, the mission did not end without difficulty. It had been planned to bring the craft back to a landing in Central Asia on the seventeenth orbit. However, a fault in the solar sensor of the attitude control system prevented firing of the retro-rocket and the crew were forced into making another complete orbit of the Earth. Re-entry was manually controlled by Belyaev. Instead of returning in the lower latitudes of Kazakhstan, the trajectory was displaced westward due to the Earth's rotation and the capsule came down perilously in a snow-covered forest near Perm in the Urals. This was some 750 miles north-east of Moscow. A communications aerial burned off during re-entry resulting in loss of contact. Nevertheless, both cosmonauts were reported to be in good health following the flight.

Belyaev later explained that they were out of the capsule within 5 min. However, it was two and a half hours before the first rescue helicopter arrived and it was extremely cold. They were taken to Perm by air the next day. Meanwhile their capsule, stated to be undamaged, was air-lifted back to the Baikonur cosmodrome.

Leonov nearly missed his chance of becoming the world's first 'space-walker'. At the end of 1963, he and his wife were returning by car to the 'Stellar Village' when the driver misjudged a corner. The vehicle left the road, ending up through the ice of a pond. Leonov struggled out rescuing his wife and the driver from under the water.

There seems little doubt that features of the Voskhod and its successors were developed in secret as part of the Cosmos programme. From a comparison of orbital parameters, it is possible to conclude that Cosmos 47 – recovered after 1 day – was a trial run for Voskhod 1 introduced 6 days later.

Few details of recoverable Cosmos satellites have been released by the Soviet authorities, and US sources believe a number have been launched for reconnaissance purposes.

Such vehicles have been observed to return their capsules over the Soviet Union after a few days. However, many of the Cosmos breed – both recoverable and non-recoverable – have legitimate scientific tasks, not least of which has been the measurement of air drag and radiation at different altitudes.

Cosmos 110, launched on 22 February 1966, helped to prepare the way for the next series of Soviet manned spacecraft. It was devoted to a thorough investigation of the working of the heart and the entire circulatory system in the space environment. On board were two dogs Veterok and Ugolek, in separate pressurized containers. The first was the principal experimental animal, the second the control animal.

The orbit achieved, inclined at 51·85° to the Equator, ranged between 118 and 548 miles, taking the craft into the region of the inner Van Allen radiation belt.

The re-entry capsule of Cosmos 110 was recovered on 16 March after a flight of nearly 22 days, with its dog-passengers 'alive and well'. Dr Boris Yegorov commented: 'We have got an answer to two main questions: Whether changes occurring in the organism represent adaptation to weightlessness; and, if such adaptation is possible, how far the organism will be able to compensate for the increased load on returning to Earth.'

Clad in special suits, which secured them in the capsule, they could nevertheless assume different positions; the suits also served to connect sensors and tubes to the animals for bio-medical studies and food delivery.

Paste-like food was introduced directly into the animals' stomachs from plastic containers by pneumatic action through artificially made openings (gastrostoms). The food, which had been tried out in advance, included meat, potatoes, flour, vitamins, and water.

Air-conditioning and regeneration systems were described as an improved modification of identical systems used during the flights of Soviet spacecraft with dog-passengers in August 1960 and March 1961.

For studying neuro-reflectory regulation of the dogs' cardio-vascular system, the capsule was equipped to measure arterial pressure, record bio-currents of the heart with the aid of ingrown electrodes, the pulse of the carotid artery, the mechanical working of the heart, and breathing. In addition electrodes were ingrown into peripheral nerves to gauge the activity of the central formations of the brain regulating the vascular tonus. Bio-medical data were telemetered to Earth to ensure timely medical control over the state of the dogs' health.

On television Dr Yegorov demonstrated the 'canine doubles' of Veterok and Ugolek. They were wearing space-jackets to which sensor leads and feeding devices were attached. He pointed out the tube grafted into a dog's aorta by means of which arterial pressure is measured. After the experiment, he said the tube would be painlessly removed without any ill-effect to the dog's vital functions. Dr Yegorov also drew attention to an orifice plate through which food is pneumatically forced into the dog's stomach. Viewers saw a plastic bag with this food weighing 600–700 grammes. One bag had enough food for 24 hr.

The long delay in Soviet manned launchings which followed the flight of Voskhod 2, therefore, did not represent a period of inactivity. Much of the intervening development was cloaked in secrecy, but clearly attention was given to perfecting an extra-vehicular spacesuit and a more reliable airlock system alongside the development of the larger spacecraft and multi-stage booster.

It is instructive to return to the comments of Yuri Gagarin at the 1963 IAF Congress. 'Techniques being developed in my country', he said, 'involve the assembly of components of space-craft in Earth-orbit and the introduction of propellant.' He said this procedure was being adopted because it was not possible to launch vehicles of several scores of tons directly to the Moon.

Then, in October, came Nikita Khrushchev's famous remark about watching the Americans reach the Moon. 'We will see how they fly there, and how they land there . . . and, most important, how they will take off and return.' Was the pace becoming too hot, or had America misjudged Soviet intentions of being first on the Moon?

Although the group flights performed by Nikolayev and Popovich in 1962 and Bykovsky and Tereshkova in 1963 were impressive, particularly in launch timing and orbital injection, they did not amount to orbital rendezvous. Gagarin himself pointed out that although it required little extra propellant to achieve rendezvous when the distance separating spacecraft was down to a few miles, there were still difficult problems affecting 'communications, optics, and manœuvre'. The Americans, of course, solved these problems in the Gemini programme with the help of radar.

Gagarin's remarks in Paris were given added point in an article he wrote commemorating the sixth anniversary of Sputnik 1. 'It may, of course, be too bold of me to conclude that interplanetary travel will be a fact within a few years. Preparations for these flights will call for a still greater effort including many more Earth-orbital flights.'

He stressed again the key nature of Earth-orbit rendezvous. When these experiments are finalized, 'we shall be able to assemble spacecraft of any size directly in flight and the refuelling problem, which is so important for protracted space journeys, will also be solved'.

When at last rumours of an impending new Soviet spaceflight began in Moscow towards the end of April 1967, they were linked with the prospect of two manned vehicles achieving a space rendezvous. In the preceding months an increased tempo of launchings in the Cosmos programme had appeared to indicate the end of unmanned testing of a spacecraft, larger than Voskhod, which would orbit at an inclination of 51–52° to the equator.

We were not long to be kept in doubt. At 0335 hours (Moscow time) on 23 April, Soyuz (Union) 1 ascended from the Baikonur cosmodrome with a single occupant, Colonel Vladimir Komarov, the man who had previously commanded the three-man Voskhod 1. The orbit, inclined at 51° 40' to the equator, ranged between 125 and 139 miles. Reliable two-way radio contact with the spacecraft was reported on frequencies of 15·008, 18·035 and 20·008 Mc/s.

According to *Tass* the mission involved testing a new piloted spacecraft; checking the craft's systems and elements in conditions of spaceflight; conducting extended scientific and physical-technical experiments and studies in conditions of spaceflight, and continuing medical and biological studies and studies of the influence of various factors of spaceflight on the human organism.

When Soyuz 1 completed its fifth orbit at 1000 hr. (Moscow time), Komarov reported that the flight programme was being

fulfilled successfully and that he was feeling well. Cabin temperature as indicated by telemetry was 16°C and cabin pressure
750 mm. of mercury—both normal. Radio communication was
stable.

Between 1320 and 2120 hr. the cosmonaut rested out of radio
contact with the command station. By 2230 hr. the craft had
completed its thirteenth revolution with Komarov reporting that
all was going to programme. At 0450 hr. on 24 April Komarov
again reported his excellent physical condition which was confirmed by telemetered data. Cabin temperature then was 17·5°C
and pressure 800 mm. of mercury. A number of set experiments
had been completed. Moscow fell silent on the flight after this
until 1723 hr. when the shock announcement came of Komarov's
death.

An official communiqué explained that the cosmonaut was in
touch with ground stations on the nineteenth orbit as he began
his re-entry over Africa reporting 'In good health, systems
functioning well.' The time was about 0600 hr. (Moscow time).
After the capsule had successfully penetrated the atmosphere
the shroud lines of its main landing parachute became entangled
at a height of some 7 km. (4·3 miles) and Komarov plunged to
his death over the Soviet Union.

Two days after the tragedy the ashes of a brave pioneer of the
space age were buried in the Kremlin wall alongside those of
Soviet statesmen.

There was no question that the accident would deflect the path
of the Soviet programme. A State Commission was immediately
set up to inquire into every aspect of the failure and ensure that
further spaceflights could proceed in safety. It was the year of
the fiftieth anniversary of the Communist Revolution and Russia
was on the brink of important space developments.

CHAPTER TWO

BRIDGE TO THE MOON

Future historians may well refer to our time as 'the era of the lunar journey'. Spawned by the missile and space rivalry that developed between Russia and America in the 1950s, its foundations in the United States were laid in 1958 when Congress passed the National Aeronautics and Space Act calling for leadership in space.

Project Apollo was sealed on 25 May 1961, by the late President Kennedy. Addressing a joint session of Congress, he said: 'I believe that this nation should commit itself to achieving the goal, before the decade is out, of landing a man on the Moon and returning him safely to Earth. No single space project in this period will be so difficult or so expensive to accomplish.'

In setting this ambitious goal, the Kennedy Administration recognized the necessity of a challenging objective. If men could be landed on the Moon, the technology involved would provide a solid base from which other space ventures could be sprung, either military or peaceful according to need.

But much of the spadework had been done earlier under the Eisenhower Administration. In October 1958, the National Aeronautics and Space Administration (NASA) had come officially into being on the basis of a reorganized National Advisory Committee on Aeronautics (NACA). Under administrator Dr T. Keith Glennan, a primary task had been to define the first American manned spacecraft, drawing upon proposals previously reviewed by NACA. The Space Task Group, initially an informal team at Langley Field, Virginia, under the direction of Dr Robert R. Gilruth, subsequently became the basis of the Manned Spacecraft Center at Houston, Texas. Contracts for the first US manned space capsule were placed by NASA in 1959. The name Mercury was chosen symbolic of the winged messenger of the gods of Roman mythology.

McDonnell Aircraft Corporation, the prime contractor,

delivered the first of an initial batch of twenty-four development capsules only fourteen months after receiving the order. These 'boiler-plate' vehicles were used for various purposes, including the test of the rocket escape system designed to pull the capsule away from its launching rocket in the event of a catastrophic failure either on the launch pad or following lift-off. These tests were assisted by solid-propellant rockets known as Little Joe. Unlike the Russian Vostok capsule the Mercury astronaut was not provided with an ejection seat. However, once the escape rocket had separated the capsule from its booster, standard recovery procedures would release the drogue and landing parachutes for a normal recovery in the sea.

Out of 508 suitably qualified jet-pilots who applied as Mercury astronauts, thirty-two were selected for preliminary physical and mental tests. On 2 April 1959, the names of the seven successful candidates were announced by NASA. They were: Lieutenant-Commander M. Scott Carpenter; Major L. Gordon Cooper, Jr; Lieutenant-Colonel John H. Glenn, Jr; Captain Virgil I. Grissom; Commander Alan B. Shepard, Jr; Commander Walter M. Schirra, Jr, and Major Donald K. Slayton. Slayton subsequently was found to have a slight heart irregularity and was removed from the roster of active astronauts. However, his function in the Mercury programme should not be minimized. He served as co-ordinator for astronaut activities, and maintained overall supervision of astronaut duties. (Another nine astronauts were chosen by NASA in September 1962 to participate in the subsequent Gemini programme.)

The first major firing of a boiler-plate Mercury capsule on an Atlas-D occurred on 9 September 1959. The test was sub-orbital and meant to subject the capsule to severe heating and airloads in ballistic flight. The test was successful and the capsule was recovered intact.

The programme did not proceed without its frustrations. Another key test was scheduled for 29 July 1960, when a production capsule would be launched unmanned from an Atlas booster on a sub-orbital flight. After travelling 1,500 miles over the Atlantic from Cape Canaveral (now Cape Kennedy), it was meant to reach its zenith some 110 miles above the Earth; the capsule would plunge back into the atmosphere at 19,000 ft/sec. enduring decelerative forces up to 16·5 g. As there was no test-subject aboard the escape system was omitted.

As it happened the booster exploded catastrophically about a minute after leaving the pad. The instrumented capsule, blown clear of the Atlas, was intact as it hit the water; NASA salvaged the wreckage.

Meanwhile, another smaller rocket called Redstone, developed by Dr Wernher von Braun's Army Group, was being pressed into service in order to gain further experience with Mercury capsules in sub-orbital flight. The rocket had the capability of boosting a capsule over a ballistic trajectory of some 200 miles reaching its peak 125 miles into space.

By this time the seven volunteer astronauts – all seasoned military test-pilots – were busily preparing for the day when they would occupy the 'hot-seat' on top of a rocket on its way into space. Much preliminary work had already been done in America with the celebrated X-series of rocket-aircraft culminating in the X-15. Bio-medical experiments had been made with animal and human test-subjects in centrifuges and rocket-sleds. As early as 1952, it was disclosed that a number of rhesus and cebus monkeys and white mice had, on occasions, been rocketed to altitudes of up to 80 miles in V-2 and Aerobee rockets.

In these pioneer experiments by the US Air Force the monkeys had been anaesthetized before take-off, a 'luxury' subsequently denied to later experimental animals. Strapped down by nylon netting on sponge-rubber beds, they were placed inside pressurized capsules 3 ft long by 15 in. diameter.

Each animal had a face-mask through which it received a recirculated supply of oxygen. Instruments attached to their bodies allowed measurement of blood-pressure, heart action, pulse, and respiration, and this information was telemetered to the ground.

Data received indicated that the monkeys were not seriously disturbed by the actual flight. However, although the capsules were successfully ejected from the rockets, only one reached the ground alive because of failure of the landing parachutes. Ironically, the one monkey that did reach the ground safely died of heat-stroke in the New Mexico desert a short time before it was located.

An Aerobee launched from Holloman Air Force Base in 1952 was particularly successful in showing the reactions of mammals under weightless conditions. Inside the nose-cone were two monkeys and two white mice. The mice travelled in a glass-walled chamber with a ciné-camera to record their behaviour. One mouse had part of the balance mechanism of the inner ear removed.

When the nose-cone was recovered and the film developed, the mice were found to have acted normally up to the time propulsion ceased, but during the 3-minute period of zero gravity they were seen in different attitudes threshing around and oddly suspended between floor and ceiling.

Dr J. P. Henry of the Wright Field Aeromedical Laboratory, under whose aegis the experiments were made, said the mice were apparently as much at ease when inverted as when upright; they merely lost the vertical reference of gravity and assumed what-ever posture was convenient. The mouse that had been deprived of its balance mechanism remained curled up in a corner of the capsule, seemingly unaware of its weightlessness.

The mice were returned to the laboratory where they were reported to be lively and breeding freely. Together with the two small monkeys, housed in separate compartments, they had endured a brief initial acceleration of 15 g, lasting less than 1 sec., and a longer force of 3 to 4 g lasting for 45 sec.

Dr Henry's conclusions, nearly a decade before the first man rocketed into space, were extraordinarily perceptive; he said pilots would have no difficulty in performing all actions necessary to control a vehicle in a weightless state.

Primates were used in a number of subsequent space experi-ments. Particularly successful, on 28 May 1959, was the ballistic flight of monkeys Able and Baker in the re-entry cone of a Jupiter IRBM launched on test down the Atlantic Missile Range. They were recovered after reaching a peak altitude of 300 miles pro-viding much useful data on zero-g effects on living organisms.

Short-term experiments in weightlessness were also performed by human subjects in aircraft. To induce weightlessness the aircraft had to be precisely controlled to fly a powered parabolic path where engine thrust and lift just counterbalanced the pull of gravity. Often it was possible to keep men weightless in the cabin for more than half a minute. This became a standard technique for astronaut training.

It was some time, however, before NASA was sufficiently confident to risk one of its human 'guinea-pigs' to the uncertainties of ballistic flight.

The very first Redstone to carry an unmanned Mercury capsule, on 21 November 1960, fizzled on the pad, lifting a few inches as engine thrust rose and then subsiding. Fortunately it did not topple. However, the spacecraft having received the shutdown signal reacted accordingly; the escape rocket fired lifting the capsule away for emergency parachute recovery. The fault was later attributed to ground umbilicals which detached from the rocket in the wrong sequence.

As the Redstone had been slightly damaged by recontact with the launcher the capsule was fitted to another rocket. A month later it made a textbook flight down the Atlantic Missile Range parachuting down into the sea some 236 miles from the Cape. Maximum height of the trajectory was 135 miles.

In the test launchings that immediately preceded the first American manned spaceflight, three stand out as significant. One occurred on 31 January 1961, when Ham, a 137-lb chimpanzee, was lobbed in the Mercury MR-2 capsule a distance of 420 miles. The performance was greater than planned because of 'excessive booster thrust', the maximum altitude being 155 miles, some 40 miles higher than envisaged in the flight programme. In fact, the capsule was driven at a speed greater than 5,000 m.p.h., much faster than intended. Improper working of the engine system, due to a jammed thrust regulator, triggered the emergency escape rocket near the end of boosted flight. This forcibly separated the capsule, adding further to the already increased velocity and range.

Despite the fact that a pressure bulkhead was punctured on

landing, the capsule was safely recovered with Ham inside. The chimpanzee had been in a miniature contoured couch inside a pressure chamber. Oxygen was introduced into the chamber, and the expired air passed through the spacecraft's environmental control system where impurities were removed before it was recirculated with added oxygen. Bio-medical data were sensed by electrodes attached to the animal, measurements being tele-metered to the ground and simultaneously tape-recorded.

Mercury chimpanzees, trained at the Aeromedical Field Laboratory, Holloman Air Force Base, New Mexico, were expected to depress two handles in response to light signals. Failure to perform was 'punished' by slight electric shocks. This helped to determine if simple tasks could be carried out during launching, weightlessness, and re-entry; also to discern psycho-logical and physiological effects on work-tasks performed under stress. The animal was photographed by a 16-mm. ciné-camera through a transparent window in the pressure chamber.

Next in the launch programme came an Atlas booster firing on 21 February 1961, to check maximum heating under the worst possible conditions of re-entry. The capsule reached a peak altitude of 108 miles, re-entering the atmosphere at a speed of about 13,000 m.p.h. It landed 1,425 miles downrange.

On 25 April 1961 – just thirteen days after Gagarin had made his celebrated circuit of the Earth – America prepared to orbit an unmanned Mercury capsule for the first time. Standing in for a live astronaut was an astronaut-simulator, 'a breathing, sweating, and talking robot'. This placed the same loads upon the environmental control system as a man would have done. It removed oxygen and added carbon dioxide and water vapour to the recirculatory oxygen, in effect duplicating the human cir-culatory and respiratory functions. Electrical heating elements added 200 W to simulate body heat. Two playback tape-recorders, each with pre-recorded voice messages of 45 min. duration, were also fitted to evaluate the communications system. The messages by-passed the normal microphone and were relayed to ground stations over the spacecraft's transmitters.

The launching, however, was disastrous. After a smooth lift-off the Atlas booster began to veer from course; after 40 sec. the range safety officer was forced to press the 'destruct' button. The radio signal triggered explosives in the rocket which blew it up.

Once again, this test showed the effectiveness of the emergency escape system. Before the booster was destroyed, sensing devices registered the booster's erratic behaviour, immediately commanding separation of the capsule and ignition of the escape rocket. The capsule separated cleanly and descended into the sea beneath its parachute. Had a man been aboard he would certainly have survived.

Despite this setback NASA pressed ahead with plans to conduct their first manned test – with a Redstone booster. Although this was to be limited to a ballistic 'lob' down the Atlantic Missile Range, similar to that made with the chimpanzee Ham, it contained all the drama of a fully fledged orbital mission.

Astronaut Alan B. Shepard spent more than four hours in his Freedom 7 capsule on 5 May 1961, while clouds dispersed and 'technical holds' were dealt with by launch technicians. At last, just after 0934 hr. EST, came the moment of truth and Shepard was away to a perfect launch.

The sequence followed exactly as planned. The Redstone made a programmed ascent, pitched over at the correct angle to accelerate away over the Atlantic and cut-off at T-plus 42 sec. It was then inclined at $40°$ to the horizontal, with a speed of about 4,500 m.p.h. and altitude 196,000 ft. After the escape tower had jettisoned, the capsule was separated by releasing a clamp ring and firing three small rockets mounted in the retro-rocket pack attached to Mercury's heat shield.

Next the capsule's periscope was extended. Then, according to programme, the automatic attitude control system turned the craft round so that the blunt heat shield was pitched up at $14·5°$ to the path of flight.

It was at this point that Shepard first demonstrated man's ability to control a spacecraft under weightless conditions. By working a control handle he gently pitched, yawed, and rolled the craft to a maximum deviation of $20°$, using bursts from gas-jet nozzles.

Shepard himself pitched up the capsule within 5° of the required angle of 34° prior to firing the three 1,160-lb.s.t. retro-rockets. When the spacecraft reached its peak altitude at 116 miles, these were fired in a 30-sec. burst, one after the other, reducing speed by some 350 m.p.h. Then the retro-rocket pack was jettisoned by detonating an explosive bolt securing steel straps.

After retracting the periscope, Shepard restored the capsule to automatic control – although he could still 'override' this with the hand controller. Finally, just before re-entering the atmosphere, he made a touch test with his right hand of certain equipment in the cabin. All the time he was under observation from a 16-mm. ciné-camera mounted above and behind his left shoulder.

Following re-entry – when Shepard experienced a maximum deceleration of above 5 g for about half a minute – the drogue parachute was ejected with radar chaff at 25,000 ft altitude. Thirty seconds later the main parachute deployed lowering the capsule into the sea at 32 ft/sec. Impact with the water was cushioned by a landing bag released from the capsule when the heat shield was detached during the landing sequence.

The records show that Shepard travelled a distance of 297 miles;* the flight lasted 15 min. 22 sec. of which he was weightless for 4 min. 45 sec.

Further valuable experience in controlling a Mercury capsule was obtained by the late Captain Virgil 'Gus' Grissom on 21 July 1961, when he performed a similar sub-orbital flight in his Liberty Bell capsule. After separating from the Redstone booster the craft reached a height of 118 miles and splashed down 303 miles downrange. As in the case of his predecessor, Grissom manually controlled the capsule's 34° attitude for firing the retro-rockets. In this he was aided by a pilot-observation window which replaced two 6-in. portholes in Freedom 7. Reference lines inscribed on the four-pane window allowed the astronaut to align the craft precisely with the horizon, and the 'picture-window'

* Earlier NASA gave the distance travelled as 302 miles and peak altitude 115 miles.

also gave a much-improved view of the Earth and the stars. Measuring 19 in. across the top it was located directly above the astronaut on the capsule's centre line.

It was after Liberty Bell had come down beneath its parachute that disaster nearly struck. As Grissom waited inside the capsule to be picked up, suddenly the escape hatch blew out and the capsule immediately began to fill with water. Grissom struggled out and had to swim for several minutes before he was rescued by a helicopter. Meanwhile, the crew of another helicopter – a Marine Sikorsky HUS-1 – had managed to get a line attached to the sinking capsule, but the struggle to save it proved too great. At one point the HUS-1 had a wheel in the water, so determined were the crew to hold on to it until a rescue ship arrived; then a red warning light (false, as it later transpired) appeared in the cockpit indicating overheating of the helicopter's engine. Connexion with Liberty Bell was severed and it sank in 18,000 ft of water.

Meanwhile, Grissom was taken aboard the USS *Randolph*. Although he had swallowed a lot of water, he quickly recovered. Later he explained that he had removed the safety pin from the escape hatch a short time before the explosive bolts which secured it blew out; apparently there had been a short-circuit.

Despite the success of the two manned sub-orbital shots, NASA had yet to get a Mercury spacecraft into orbit. On 13 September 1961, a capsule carrying an astronaut-simulator was boosted into space on the nose of an Atlas; after separating it was successfully orientated by ground control; the retro-rockets fired as planned near the end of the first orbit, and it landed in the sea about 160 miles east of Bermuda.

Then, on 29 November, came the turn of chimpanzee Enos to make an orbital flight in an Atlas-boosted spacecraft. The orbit achieved, inclined at 32°30' to the Equator, ranged between an altitude of 100 and 147 miles. However, although intended to perform 3 revolutions of the Earth, telemetry signals indicated overheating and an orientation fault affecting roll control. The capsule therefore was commanded down after 2 orbits; it made a successful return into the Atlantic 220 miles south of Bermuda.

Now, at last, came the opportunity to launch an American into orbit. The man was Lieutenant-Colonel John Glenn of the US Marine Corps; his 3 orbits of the Earth on 20 February 1962 were a milestone in the development of manned spaceflight. However, the mission was not without its problems and it could well have ended disastrously.

After spending 3 hr. 44 min. in the Friendship 7 capsule on the launch pad, due to a series of 'technical holds', Glenn lifted off at 0947 hr. EST. The Atlas-D booster made its pre-programmed ascent over the Atlantic and at 1000 hr. came confirmation that the capsule had been successfully injected into orbit. Glenn was orbiting between 100 and 163 miles above the Earth, with an inclination of 32·5° to the Equator; this was declared good for at least 7 circuits although only 3 were attempted.

All went smoothly during the first revolution. Having entered orbit 503 miles downrange from Cape Canaveral, 20 min. later he was leaving the east coast of Africa to enter the night side of the Earth over the Indian Ocean. At 1025 hr. he consumed food paste from a tube, and at 1043 hr. he was in contact with the tracking station at Muchea, Australia, reporting he had sighted the 'bright lights' of Perth. At 1050 hr. Mercury Control gave the reassuring information that Glenn's heart-beat and respiration were 'completely normal'.

Just after 1100 hr. while approaching the Californian coast, he watched a glorious sunrise to be greeted with the strange sight of 'thousands of luminous particles' around the capsule.

Friendship 7 completed its first orbit at 1121 hr. at an average speed of 17,545 m.p.h. At 1128 hr. Glenn reported difficulties with the automatic attitude control system. The capsule was drifting off in yaw to the right at about 1°/sec. After yawing about 20°, it swung back to zero.

Glenn switched to the Fly-by-Wire system which allowed him to take overriding manual control. By manipulating the control handle he found he could stop the yawing motion and so conserve precious hydrogen peroxide fuel. After the flight it was suspected that the feed to a yaw attitude control nozzle had become clogged causing the capsule to yaw repeatedly to the right. When the 20° dispersion limit of the system was reached, the capsule was pushed back by the high-thrust jet.

The big problem, however, was yet to come. As Glenn was on his third and final orbit, the Muchea ground station picked up a telemetry signal indicating that the capsule's heat shield might have become detached due to a faulty switch. The reason for having a detachable heat shield was related to the final stages of recovery, when the capsule was suspended from its parachute just before coming down in the sea. The shield dropped down 4 ft pulling out a perforated skirt of rubberized glass-fibre; this formed an air-cushion to mitigate the landing impact.

If this shield became detached in orbit there would be nothing to prevent the craft from burning up as it re-entered the atmosphere. Mercury Control calmly discussed the position with Glenn. It was decided to keep the retro-rocket pack on the centre of the heat shield as the spacecraft re-entered the atmosphere. Normally, of course, the retro-rocket pack was jettisoned after retro-fire, being secured to the base of the capsule over the heat shield by three metal bands, released by detonating a single explosive bolt at its centre. But if the shield *had* become detached, these bands might serve to hold it in position long enough for air pressure to retain it.

Glenn described this frightening situation when I interviewed him for BBC's Ten O'Clock programme. After retro-firing at 1420 hr. EST, with the capsule some 600 miles west of Los Angeles, the first effects of re-entry became apparent some minutes later. As the capsule began to feel the effects of frictional heating suddenly there was a 'bump'. Apparently this was a steel retaining strap breaking, but at the time Glenn thought the retro-pack had jettisoned. As heating increased an orange glow appeared outside the cabin, and it quickly became apparent that something was disintegrating on the outside of the shield. Flaming chunks of debris up to 8 in. across, glowing bright orange, streamed past the window.

As Glenn believed the retro-pack had gone, he wondered if the heat shield itself might be tearing up. In fact it *was* the retro-pack, and happily Glenn survived to tell the tale. His spacecraft splashed down in the Atlantic some 210 miles north-west of San Juan, Puerto Rico, at 1443 hr. EST having covered a total distance of 80,966 miles. Ironically, it was later discovered that the fault had been illusionary; the heat shield was securely attached all the time.

Examining this capsule after the flight one could judge for oneself the rigours of the mission. The heat shield was pitted and charred, flaking in layers, but still there was a good inch of ablative material round the edge. The outer skin of the capsule, though blackened by heat, was structurally sound. This was much the same as had been experienced on previous unmanned orbital missions. Normally, the shield was subjected to a maximum temperature of around $1,650°$ C at 25 miles altitude, with the capsule moving at nearly 15,000 m.p.h.; the conical section of the spacecraft behind the bow wave of plasma received a maximum of $927°$ C.

Glenn's capsule, much lighter than the Soviet Vostok, weighed 4,265 lb at lift-off. By the time it had arrived in orbit, mainly due to removal of the escape tower, this had reduced to 2,987 lb. At the time of recovery it was 2,422 lb. Two main factors accounted for the greater weight of the Soviet vehicle. It had a re-entry capsule of larger internal volume, and it employed more rugged constructional techniques. This was partly due to the Soviet decision to use standard atmosphere in the cabin at normal pressure, whereas American designers had adopted an all-oxygen system at 5 p.s.i. pressure (see page 205).

Despite Glenn's preoccupations with the capsule, he calmly reported instrument readings to ground stations, and made observations of the Earth and the stars. He remarked on different patterns in ocean currents, such as the Gulf Stream, and he described in some detail the area north-west of El Paso, Texas, remarking on the large area of desert and its squares of irrigated land.

The enforced tasks of this flight proved beyond doubt the ability of a well-trained astronaut to work under zero-g conditions as an inherent part of the spacecraft system. Glenn him-

self thought it might be possible to use considerably less auto-
mation on future flights and this was amply demonstrated in the
later Gemini programme when the first human-controlled spacecraft were manœuvred in missions involving orbital rendezvous.

Three months later another Mercury capsule stood ready on
its Atlas booster at the Cape. This was Aurora 7 with Lieutenant-
Commander M. Scott Carpenter. Launched at 0845 hr. EDT on
24 May 1962, the craft orbited between altitudes of 100 and 169
miles at 32·5° inclination. Carpenter had been instructed to use
the Fly-by-Wire system, in which he had overriding manual
control, and to keep the purely automatic system in reserve.

The first problem encountered concerned overheating of the
pressure suit. After exercising with a rubber cord the suit temperature reached 27·8°C during the first orbit. Carpenter was
asked to relax his efforts, to get the temperature down; he did
so and it gradually dropped below 21°C.

While still on the first orbit over the Western Pacific, the astronaut switched off the orientation system to conserve fuel, allowing
the spacecraft to drift in the manner of an unstabilized satellite.
This left him free to concentrate on other tasks. After taking his
first paste meal from a tube, he looked for Glenn's mysterious
luminous particles. As the capsule approached the US coast from
over the Pacific, he noticed some, like 'snowflakes', but they were
not in the numbers Glenn had described.

Apart from instrument readings and a heavy programme of
photography, which included separation of the Atlas stage,
features of the Earth's surface and cloud cover, and luminous
particles, Carpenter had two important experiments to perform,
turning his craft into a rudimentary physics laboratory.

The most elaborate involved a Mylar plastic aluminized balloon 20 in. in diameter, which had to be released from the capsule
at the beginning of the second orbit, on the end of a 100-ft line.
A mechanical arm, to which the line was anchored, was designed
to measure any slight pull on the balloon due to drag effects. The
balloon – which had five panels of different colours – was meant
to help estimate distances in space and also to determine the
most easily recognizable colour under different conditions of

illumination. This, of course, had much to do with forthcoming experiments in orbital rendezvous and docking.

However, although the balloon deployed as planned, it did not fully inflate. Carpenter reported no effect on the spacecraft's drift; the line was sometimes taut and sometimes slack. Most brilliant when illuminated by the Sun were the orange and silver segments. The other panels on the balloon were white, yellow, and phosphorescent, the last being used to assist observation at night. A number of multi-coloured $\frac{1}{4}$-in. diameter Mylar discs, released from the folds of the balloon, were used to provide a comparison with the luminous particles. The balloon, having failed to release in orbit, trailed behind the spacecraft as it re-entered and burned up.

As a further aid to the Gemini programme, an experiment was also provided for the observation of liquid both in a weightless environment and when the retro-rockets were fired prior to re-entry. Mounted in the cabin was a 3-in. diameter flask with a central stand-pipe; three holes in the base of the pipe allowed passage of the liquid which comprised distilled water, green dye, an aerosol solution to reduce surface tension, and a silicone additive to inhibit foaming.

The flask was filmed by the astronaut-observer camera. Under zero-g, the liquid was expected to rise in the stand-pipe due to surface tension, rather than float about in globules. The results were related to the design of spacecraft tanks and restartable engine systems.

Thus, in many ways, the flight of Aurora 7 was a demonstration in miniature of the function of a manned orbiting laboratory.

However, Carpenter had his share of troubles. Apart from overheating of the spacesuit during the first and second orbits, a fault developed in the pitch horizon scanner and inadvertent use was made of two attitude control systems simultaneously, including the high-thrust system. Fuel was conserved by allowing the spacecraft to drift for 77 min. beyond the time scheduled in the flight plan.

Difficulties with the automatic attitude system meant that Carpenter had to pitch up the craft at the correct angle for retro-fire using the manual controls. Radar tracking data indicated that, in the period approaching retro-fire, the spacecraft 'had an average yaw error of 27°'. This, combined with late ignition of the retro-rockets, resulted in the capsule overshooting its scheduled landing point in the Pacific by 250 nautical miles. Carpenter pushed the manual retro-fire button when the retro-rockets did not fire automatically. This was 3–4 sec. later than planned, which accounted for 15 to 20 miles of the total overshoot error.

Then, despite the fact that a new radio frequency was being used in an attempt to defeat the radio blackout caused by the ionized sheath of plasma which forms around a spacecraft as it re-enters the atmosphere, radio contact was lost. While the world anxiously awaited news of the astronaut, at last came word that Carpenter had been located some 125 miles north-east of Puerto Rico. Having landed at 1741 hr. EDT, he had emerged from his capsule and awaited pick-up in his emergency dinghy. The flight, lasting 3 orbits, covered a total distance of 81,325 miles.

Lessons learned by Carpenter were quickly applied to the next Mercury mission. They included provision of a switch to isolate the high-thrust attitude control jets and revised fuel management training procedures.

Next to go into space from Cape Canaveral was Commander Walter M. Schirra. Lifting off at 0815 hr. EDT on 3 October 1962, he travelled in the capsule Sigma 7. His initial orbit ranged between 101 and 177 miles.

The mission, planned to last nearly 6 orbits, allowed more time for observations and experiments. A primary aim was to discover how much fuel in the H_2O_2 orientation system could be conserved. As Schirra started on his third orbit he reported that the capsule still had 90 per cent of its fuel supply. The capsule was allowed to drift in attitude with all controls switched off for 99 min. of the flight programme. The only anomaly was elevated suit temperature experienced during the first 2 hr.; this was later attributed to a foreign substance in a control valve.

Of the experiments, three high-intensity flares ignited at the Woomera rocket range were not directly observed because of intervening cloud cover. It had been hoped that, with the aid of a photometer, Schirra could establish the degree of atmospheric attenuation of a light source of known intensity. All Schirra saw above the clouds was a diffused 'block of light'.

Many photographs of the Earth were obtained using a 35-mm. ciné-camera. Scientists, having examined pictures taken by previous astronauts, were interested in obtaining colour photographs of fold mountains, fault regions, volcanic fields, meteorite impacts, and glaciers. They were also keen to study the photometric properties of various land surfaces for comparison with features of the Moon and other planets.

Schirra also saw fluorescent particles, or 'snowflakes'; he said he could produce them by banging on the walls of the cabin. Another subject of interest was the type and magnitude of the interaction of nuclear particles in the space environment; two radiation-sensitive emulsion packs were mounted on each side of the astronaut's couch.

Test samples of heat-resistant materials were bonded to the cylindrical neck of the capsule for post-flight examination. Some had discrete cracks or slots, half of which had been filled or repaired. In this way it was hoped to discover the effectiveness of possible repairs made to spacecraft structures.

Apart from a 2-sec. delay in retro-fire, the spacecraft made an uneventful return into the Earth's atmosphere, landing in the Pacific Ocean some 295 miles north-east of Midway Island at 1728 hr. EDT. The distance covered was about 153,900 miles.

Last in the Mercury series was the most ambitious and in many ways the most successful. It was planned as America's first daylong spaceflight, with the aim of achieving 22 orbits. With astronaut Major L. Gordon Cooper at the controls of capsule Faith 7, lift-off came at 0904 hr. EDT on 15 May 1963, with the vehicle entering an orbit ranging from 100 to 166 miles.

As in the case of astronauts Glenn, Carpenter, and Schirra, Cooper had many control tasks to perform. Also, because of the prolonged period spent under weightlessness, special importance was attached to medical studies.

The first orbit was largely devoted to checking proper function of the spacecraft and radio communication with the ground. Cooper observed the lights of Perth, Australia, and received the 'go' signal for 7 orbits. However, irregular behaviour of the pressure suit heat exchanger on this and subsequent orbits led to abandonment of the prearranged 8-hr. rest programme. Cooper said he dozed periodically for 10 to 15 min. throughout the mission.

On the second orbit blood-pressure was measured and the astronaut performed exercises using elastic cords. He took his first 10-min. nap. On the third orbit a battery-powered 5·75-in. diameter sphere, with two flashing xenon lights, was released from the retro-pack into space. The lights flashed at about once per sec. and Cooper was able to observe them on the night side of the fourth and fifth orbits. Again this experiment, related to later Gemini and Apollo missions, helped to judge distances in space. As the light intensity and separation speed were known, it was possible to obtain visual sighting data up to about 15 miles.

At the beginning of the fifth orbit, a cabin temperature test was made with the coolant system inoperative, while the astronaut relied on the suit cooling circuit alone. This provided engineering data for the design of future heat exchanger systems.

Near Bloemfontein in South Africa a 3,000,000-candlepower xenon light, switched on for 3 min., was observed on the fifth orbit; also lights of the near-by city. This was mainly to check the feasibility of using ground or high-altitude lights as navigation fixes for mid-course and near-Earth corrections in project Apollo; also to give some indication of light attenuation through the atmosphere. On a number of orbits radiation measurements were taken; and during the sixth the balloon experiment, only partly successful in the Carpenter mission, was tried again. This time the multi-coloured Mylar balloon failed to eject.

Meals on the extended Mercury mission were more varied. There was 'ready-to-eat', bite-sized food 'in sufficient quantity to satisfy all calorific requirements', and the experimental, Gemini-type, dehydrated food and drink prepacked in plastic containers for reconstitution during the flight.

Preparation of the dehydrated food required the addition of

water. The containers were fitted with nozzles through which water was added; food (or drink) was forced out of the same nozzles after hydration. The drink was ready for consumption shortly after water was added; the food required about 5 min. of mixing. Cooper carried a food supply totalling 2,376 calories, including such meals as spaghetti and meat sauce and a beef and gravy dinner.

After taking refreshment during the seventh orbit and exercising, he received the 'go' signal for a further 10 orbits. Between the tenth and thirteenth orbits Cooper slept, awakening on the fourteenth without a signal. After making routine reports he ate and drank, and an orbit later began a series of observations including dim-light phenomena and horizon definition photography. Cooper was then given clearance for the scheduled 22 orbits.

More observations were made as the flight progressed, including infra-red weather photography. Cooper also saw the luminous 'snowflakes' but concluded they were created by moisture particles formed by hydrogen peroxide vapour from the spacecraft's attitude control nozzles.

But by far the most remarkable observations reported by Cooper were those concerned with detail on the ground which, according to the laws of optics, were 'impossible'. Apart from seeing rivers, lakes, mountains, and islands while over North Africa, he saw what he thought was the wake of a boat on the Nile. Looking down from his capsule over Northern India and Tibet, he spotted winding roads, wisps of smoke from chimneys, houses, road vehicles, and a train.

Space officials were incredulous and after the flight there was talk of space-illusions and hallucination. It was not until Cooper's subsequent Gemini mission with 'Pete' Conrad that the arguments were finally settled.

Meanwhile, coming near the end of his prolonged orbital flight, Cooper had other matters to concern him. Difficulties with the spacecraft's orientation system necessitated him taking over manual control. The trouble arose with two connexions to an amplifier-calibrator which served to convert electrical signals of various spacecraft systems into commands. Part of this unit's function was to relay commands to activate H_2O_2 thrusters in the automatic attitude control system. The fault was subsequently traced to moisture in the spacecraft causing corrosion in and around electrical connexions.

Cooper pitched up the spacecraft using the manual controls and fired the retro-rockets. After the electrical failure, he was also instructed by Mercury Control to complete the re-entry phase on manual. Instructions for retro-sequence checks, manœuvres, and timing were provided by astronaut John Glenn acting as spacecraft communicator aboard the tracking ship *Coastal Sentry* offshore of Japan.

Splash-down came about 80 miles south-east of Midway Island in the Pacific at 1924 hr. EDT on 16 May. The capsule was clearly seen descending by parachute from the aircraft carrier *Kearsarge* which secured recovery some 37 min. later. Cooper had travelled a distance of 583,469 miles.

Despite significant progress made in the Mercury programme, America was trailing badly in man-hours spent in space. Of the six US astronauts only four had made orbital flights lasting a total of 53 hr. Between them they had covered a distance of 900,000 miles. In contrast Soviet Vostok cosmonauts had logged 382 hr. Valentina Tereshkova alone had been in space 17 hr. longer than all the US astronauts put together.

It was some two years before the Americans began to reverse this situation in the brilliantly executed Gemini programme.

Once again McDonnell Aircraft Corporation was made prime contractor by NASA. This time the vehicle had to sustain two men, with the astronauts having full manual control of orbital manœuvre. Moreover, by offsetting the vehicle's centre of mass, it was required to generate a proportion of aerodynamic lift during re-entry giving the ability to steer the vehicle more precisely towards a fixed landing point. Gemini was named after the constellation containing the two stars Castor and Pollux, the 'heavenly twins'.

After extensive ground testing the launch programme began on 8 April 1964, when a two-stage Titan 2, adapted from the

ICBM – which now took over manned spacecraft launching from Atlas – sent an unmanned Gemini into orbit from Cape Kennedy.

This initial test was purely to evaluate launch-vehicle/spacecraft compatibility. There was no attempt to separate the spacecraft from the rocket's final stage. The orbit, angled at 33° to the Equator, was slightly higher than expected; it ranged between 100 and 204 miles. Nevertheless, all flight objectives were met and 104 instrument measurements were received during the first orbit.

The next flight, still unmanned, came on 19 January 1965, when a Gemini capsule was launched over a sub-orbital trajectory, this time separating from the rocket in order to test the capsule's re-entry behaviour. After reaching an altitude of some 99 miles and surviving the rigours of frictional heating the craft parachuted down into the Atlantic and was recovered.

So successful were the results of these preliminary tests that the first manned Gemini flight (GT-3) was launched on 23 March 1965. Lifting-off from Cape Kennedy at 0924 hr. EST, following 'technical holds' lasting only 24 min., the initial orbit, angled at 33° to the Equator, ranged between 100 and 139 miles. Aboard were the late Virgil I. Grissom, command pilot, and John W. Young. Orbiting the Earth three times in 4 hr. 53 min., theirs was the first manned spacecraft to be manœuvred out of one orbit into another. This was achieved by using the high-thrust control rockets aboard the spacecraft worked by manual controls. How this affected succeeding orbits can be seen from the fact that on the second orbit, perigee and apogee distances were 98–105 miles, and on the third 100–140 miles. Adjustment of orbital height or small plane changes were accomplished by controlled bursts from 85-lb and 100-lb thrust chambers working in conjunction with 25-lb thrusters providing control in pitch, yaw, and roll. The propellant for all these motors was nitrogen tetroxide (oxidiser) and monomethylhydrazine (fuel).

Splash-down came at 1417 hr. EST in the Atlantic Ocean not far from Grand Turk Island. The distance travelled was about 80,000 miles. In this mission Grissom, who had previously made the second sub-orbital Mercury flight in 1961, became the first man to enter space for a second time.

Next into orbit were James A. McDivitt and the late Edward H. White II. Lift-off occurred at 1016 hr. EST on 3 June 1965, with the Gemini 4 spacecraft entering an orbit ranging between 100 and 175 miles. One of the first objects of this mission was to rendezvous with the second stage of the Titan launch vehicle, after separation of the spacecraft, using Gemini's ability to manœuvre under rocket thrust. This proved abortive. McDivitt said the rocket casing fell away too rapidly; it was also turning over at 40 to 50 deg./sec. – 'much faster than anyone had anticipated'. In a vain attempt to chase the booster about 42 per cent of the available fuel was consumed. It was suggested that a successful rendezvous might depend on the use of radar and a larger fuel supply. When the manœuvres were finally called off, the spacecraft was orbiting between 103 and 182 miles above the Earth.

The planned extra-vehicular activity of astronaut White was delayed from the second to the third orbit to allow more time to prepare for the experiment. In the pure oxygen environment of Gemini's cabin at 5 p.s.i., McDivitt helped White put on his special equipment, which included an emergency oxygen chest pack. Finally, both astronauts pressurized their suits at 3·7 p.s.i.

After the cabin had been depressurized, at 1442 hr. EST the hatch was opened on White's side. Three minutes later the astronaut climbed out of the hatch and using a hand-held gas-gun gently launched himself into space, his only restraint being a 25-ft umbilical tether. The tether also contained the oxygen supply hose and electrical leads; it had a Mylar aluminized and nylon covering.

White found manœuvring with the gas-gun comparatively simple, but as its fuel was exhausted after 3 min. he spent the remainder of his time 'getting the feel of space' by twisting his body, moving his arms and legs, and pulling on the tether to induce tumbling motions. There were no disturbing reactions and, in fact, White having described the experience as 'exhilarating' remained outside longer than planned – 21 min. His pulse at the start of EVA was 150 and just before re-entering the spacecraft it was 178. After some difficulty in resealing the hatch, it was finally closed at 1506 hr. and the cabin repressurized.

The flight of Gemini 4 was also significant in other ways. On the Earth White reported seeing roads, boat wakes, strings of street lights, airfield runways, and smoke from trains and buildings. Many observations and tests were made during the 4-day mission, not least of these being related to bio-medical effects. At the time, particularly with regard to Soviet results, there had been some anxiety concerning prolonged exposure to weightlessness and its influence on the human cardiovascular system. However, although both men had temporarily reduced blood-pressure after the flight, medical tests gave no indication that adequately prepared people could not safely endure spaceflights of longer duration.

Although a fault in the spacecraft's computer did not allow the spacecraft to make a semi-lifting re-entry, the ballistic return was sufficiently accurate to place the vehicle some 45 miles from the appointed landing place 390 miles east of Cape Kennedy and 230 miles north of San Salvador. The splash-down came at 1212 hr. EST on 7 June, the spacecraft having made 62 revolutions* of the Earth and covered a distance of 1,609,700 miles.

The next mission, planned to last 8 days, was to investigate the problems of orbital rendezvous in more detail. It was also the first mission to use fuel-cells instead of chemical batteries to supply electrical power. Aboard Gemini 5 were L. Gordon Cooper, Jr., and Charles Peter Conrad. This time there were no 'technical holds' and the Titan rocket lifted the capsule off the pad at precisely 0900 hr. EST on 21 August 1965, achieving an initial orbit of 101 to 217 miles.

First task was to release from the spacecraft's adapter module a 76-lb Radar Evaluation Pod (REP). This device embodied the same type of radar system then being developed for incorporation in Agena spacecraft for full-scale rendezvous and docking experiments. Although the target was released, rendezvous

---

* At this time NASA began to count Earth revolutions rather than orbits, this being defined as the number of passes over the longitude of the launch site.

manœuvres were frustrated by troubles which developed in Gemini 5 affecting the fuel-cell electrical power supply. The fuel-cells themselves, developed by General Electric, worked perfectly; the trouble stemmed from a simple heater fault in the cryogenic oxygen tank. This led to excessive heat transfer into the hydrogen tank, and it was feared that the cells would produce too much water (the by-product of the reaction) which could swamp the system. After the trouble first arose, probably during the launch period, tank pressure had dropped from 850 to 60 p.s.i.

Nevertheless, the Radar Evaluation Pod was released shortly after entering the night side of the Earth on the second orbit and a number of infra-red and radar measurements were made. However, the pressure drop in the spacecraft's fuel-cells became so alarming that the planned manœuvre exercises had to be abandoned. So serious was the situation that emergency plans were made to return the spacecraft during the sixth orbit. Meanwhile, NASA and McDonnell teams estimated that if the oxygen tank pressure could be stabilized at around 60 p.s.i. it would gradually build up from that point. McDonnell engineers actually demonstrated the restorative powers of a duplicate set of fuel-cells under simulated space conditions as the flight progressed, and the astronauts were given the 'go' signal for another day in space on the strength of the results. As predicted, oxygen tank pressure built up steadily as the mission progressed, and the scheduled 8-day flight was allowed to proceed to its close.

The radar target by now had been lost in space. However, on the third day, ground control arranged a rendezvous exercise involving a 'phantom' target. The astronauts demonstrated they could arrive at a given point in space with an accuracy of 0·2 miles within 2 min. of the planned arrival time.

But more troubles were in store. Excessive heat transfer into the hydrogen reactant tank, causing it to vent for the latter part of the mission, led to the spacecraft building up yaw and roll rates which at times were as great as 12 deg./sec. These had to be corrected by the astronauts using the attitude control jets.

On the sixth day of the flight two left yaw thrusters became inoperative probably due to freezing of the nitrogen tetroxide supply. Later, four more attitude control thrusters stopped working, it is believed due to fuel depletion.

But troubles dogged the mission right to the end. Ground errors, fed into the spacecraft's computer, affecting the craft's inertial co-ordinates at the time of retro-fire, led to the spacecraft falling short of its planned landing point by 103 miles and some 10 miles to the right of the ground track. However, the craft made a satisfactory approach, splashing down at 0756 hr. EST on 29 August some 335 miles south-west of Bermuda and about 760 miles east of Cape Kennedy.

Gemini 5 completed 120 revolutions of the Earth during this epic mission, at last surpassing the 119-hr. spaceflight performed by the Soviet cosmonaut Valery Bykovsky in Vostok 5. The total distance travelled was 3,338,000 miles.

An enormous amount of information was put on file by the Gemini 5 astronauts despite all their frustrations. Not least was final and overwhelming proof of the ability to pick out small objects on the Earth's surface. At the Sixteenth Congress of the International Astronautical Federation, held in Athens a month later, I asked Cooper about the smallest detail he had been able to discern from orbit, reminding him of the scepticism which greeted his previous observations from the Mercury spacecraft. He said it was possible even to see the wakes of ships at sea. One of the vessels identified was a recovery ship in the Atlantic. Conrad chipped in: 'This time he had a witness.'

At the Space Congress Conrad showed photographs, taken with specially adapted commercial cameras, which also contained remarkable detail. A score of beautiful colour shots illustrated areas of the United States, Mexico, Cuba, China, Tibet, Greece, and Crete. Taken through the cabin window with the nose of Gemini tilted straight down they were obtained with a hand-held 70-mm. Hasselblad. Surface photographs of still higher resolution were made with a 35-mm. Zeiss Contarex fitted with a Questar telephoto lens with a focal length of 56 in.; a system of mirrors 'folds' the light beam into a barrel 8 in. long. In this case the camera was fixed to a bracket behind the spacecraft's right-hand window.

The astronauts had been given a list of subjects to photograph, all within the United States and Africa. They included selected cities, railways, roads, harbours, rivers, lakes, illuminated sites on the Earth's night side, ships, and wakes.

High-resolution pictures taken over Cape Kennedy showed launch sites and earthworks connected with project Apollo in surprising detail. They were detailed enough to show a causeway and a bridge across the Banana River linking Cape Kennedy with Merritt Island. Conrad said they were able to pick out every launch pad along the coast with the naked eye, including 'good old pad 19' from which their own mission had begun. At one point a white line was identified as the freeway into El Paso. If you use a magnifying glass on the picture you can see Biggs Air Force Base and El Paso International Airport. 'Although we were 100 miles up,' Conrad said, 'each morning we could see the same aircraft of a scheduled flight going into an airport by picking up its contrail. One day we even saw an aircraft ahead of its contrail.'

But even more remarkable was the astronauts' ability to spot two Minuteman ballistic missiles deliberately launched on test as Gemini passed near US launch centres. Cooper said they saw smoke and flame from one missile as it pierced the cloud deck. For a time they lost the trail and then picked it up again in the airglow and watched it to the point of burnout. The second Minuteman, seen at a slant-range of 250–300 miles, was also located by its engine flame. After losing it for a moment they found that the Sun threw a shadow of the contrail against the cloud tops.

Orbiting above Holloman Air Force Base they spotted the plume of spray thrown up by a rocket sled during water braking. The sled, too, had been fired to synchronize with their orbital pass.

Whereas previous estimates for the resolving power of the human eye, with black and white contrast, were about 1 min. of arc, these observations demonstrated an ability to resolve a half a minute or less. Before men went into space a minor degradation in visual acuity had been forecast. Similarly, photographs taken from orbit, rather than being less definitive, have tended to be more distinct than pictures taken from high-flying aircraft. Indeed, geological features in the Earth's crust show up clearly in pictures obtained from orbit which would go unnoticed in photographs taken from the air.

On the basis of Cooper's original Mercury observations his visual acuity from orbit had been measured as 20/12 on the Snellen scale, conventional 'perfect' eyesight on Earth being 20/20.

Several explanations have been offered concerning the ability to perceive objects subtending such minute visual angles. According to Dr Eugene B. Konecci of the National Aeronautics and Space Administration, one concerns the possibility that the Earth's atmosphere acts as a huge refracting medium leading to vastly improved visual observation of objects on Earth directly below the orbiting astronaut. A second theory indicates that objects with long extensions (such as aircraft vapour trails, railway tracks, and smoke rising from chimneys) facilitate observation of tiny objects at the end point. A third explanation is involved with an integration of stimuli in the central nervous system. Possibly all three theories may be jointly involved.

After the 8-day mission of Gemini 5, at last came the day when a full-scale rendezvous would be attempted with an Agena target vehicle. Some 90 min. after the Atlas-Agena had been launched on 25 October 1965, Gemini 6 was to follow with the aim of making contact on the third orbit.

As astronauts Walter M. Schirra and Thomas P. Stafford waited in their spacecraft following the launch of the target rocket, downrange tracking stations reported loss of contact. Apparently, the Agena stage, having separated from the Atlas booster, had failed to inject itself into orbit.

The launching of Gemini 6 was promptly abandoned; and as another Agena target vehicle was not available, plans were made for two manned Gemini spacecraft to perform a double flight; this to include rendezvous.

Gemini 7, to be launched first with astronauts Frank Borman and James Lovell, was to attempt a 14-day mission as a final test of man's long-term adaptability to the space environment.

Lift-off came at 1230.03 hr. EST on 4 December 1965, again without 'technical holds'. The initial orbit ranged between 100 and 204 miles angled at 28·9° to the Equator.

Apart from extensive bio-medical tests the crew were to conduct some 20 experiments, 14 of which were repeats of those conducted on former missions. For the first time new lightweight removable pressure suits were worn; each weighed only about 16 lb. Three of the medical tests included study of calcium balance, two were navigation tests in preparation for project Apollo, and there was also a laser experiment. The laser test failed as the astronauts could not identify the ground-based argon gas laser beacon.

In preparation for the rendezvous experiment, a rendezvous transponder (similar to that used in the REP and Agena target vehicle) was fitted in the small end of the spacecraft. Weighing less than 50 lb, this was designed to receive signals from the rendezvous radar system in Gemini 6 and return them at specific frequencies and pulse width.

After a heavy experimental programme lasting 5 days, Borman and Lovell made preparations for the arrival of Gemini 6 which, on the morning of 12 December, stood ready for lift-off at Cape Kennedy. They waited in vain; premature release of an inhibitor plug from the launch vehicle stopped the launching, and the scheduled 'meeting in space' was deferred for 3 whole days.

However, when at last lift-off came at 0837.26 hr. EST on 15 December, there were no pre-launch difficulties. The craft went unerringly into an orbit ranging between 100 and 162 miles, at the same orbital inclination as Gemini 7. The orbit of the first spacecraft had already been circularized at 185 miles altitude in readiness for the rendezvous experiment.

At the point of starting rendezvous manœuvres Gemini 6 was some 1,200 miles behind Gemini 7. Working from the basis of computed ground-tracking data astronaut Schirra began a series of thrust corrections using the manœuvre rockets some 94 min.

into the flight. After 6 major impulses giving 14·2 to 60·8 ft/sec. velocity changes and several smaller corrective bursts of thrust, the two craft were in radar contact at a distance of 270 miles. From that point further bursts of thrust from the manœuvre motors brought Gemini 6 to within 120 ft of Gemini 7, 5 hr. 47 min. into the flight. Despite all the anticipated problems, the astronauts used only 175 lb of their fuel supply – about half the amount allocated for rendezvous manœuvres.

The two craft remained in close formation for 20·4 hr., during which time the astronauts could see and signal to each other through their windows. Although the craft had no provision for docking, the distance between them was repeatedly brought down to a few feet. At one stage they were within a foot of each other, but the astronauts had agreed before the flight that the spacecraft would not actually touch.

After the rendezvous experiment, the Gemini 6 astronauts modified their orbit in preparation for re-entry. It had been planned in advance that their mission would not last longer than a day, and the craft was fitted with conventional batteries instead of oxygen-hydrogen fuel-cells. Gemini 6 splashed down in the Atlantic at 1029.09 hr. EST on 16 December having completed 17 revolutions of the Earth in a flight extending 449,800 miles.

Gemini 7, meanwhile, still functioning normally, maintained its experimental programme. NASA later confirmed that 75 per cent of the prescribed tests and observations had been conducted. These included spotting from orbit – visually and with the help of instruments – a submarine-launched Polaris A-3, and the re-entry vehicle of a Minuteman 2. The radiation signatures were measured by a radiometer.

Although minor problems occurred affecting the fuel-cells and attitude control system, these did not hamper operations. The new spacesuits worked particularly well, and long periods were spent with them off. The astronauts agreed this added greatly to their comfort and mobility; and Lovell, who spent more time in this 'shirt-sleeve environment', not only slept better than his companion but had a lower average heart-rate.

Splash-down for the Gemini 7 astronauts came at 0905.06 hr. EST on 18 December. Their record-breaking mission of 206 revolutions had lasted 330 hr. 35 min. 17 sec., an enormous leap in human space endeavour. The landing 700 miles south-west of Bermuda, only 7 miles from the appointed target, was the most accurate in the Gemini programme so far. The total flight distance was an impressive 5,716,900 miles.

The next vital step in the Gemini programme was to achieve rendezvous and docking, the objective that had been frustrated the previous October by the loss of the Agena target vehicle. Gemini astronauts had been learning to master the technique with a Docking Trainer at the Manned Spacecraft Center at Houston, Texas.

On 16 March 1966, another Agena target was launched by an Atlas-D from Cape Kennedy, and this time headed into space to achieve the planned 185-mile circular orbit angled at 28·9° to the Equator. To ensure that both vehicles orbited in the same plane, the launch azimuth of Gemini-Titan 8 was matched with Agena's orbit. As the target vehicle arrived in the precalculated position in space 101 min. after lift-off, Gemini 8 with astronauts Neil A. Armstrong and David R. Scott was launched in pursuit. The time was 1142.02 hr. EST, and the objective a 3-day mission including another experiment – by astronaut Scott – in extra-vehicular activity (EVA).

Initially the flight went remarkably well. The achieved orbit ranged between 100 and 168 miles, and this was successfully modified to bring the two craft into close proximity on the fourth orbit. After a short period of station-keeping during the next orbit, Armstrong prepared to complete the docking manoeuvre. The object was to nudge the small end of Gemini, by means of steering jets, into the docking collar of Agena when an index bar on the spacecraft should engage a 'V' notch or slot. In line with the slot on the Agena vehicle was the vertical antenna for the L-band radar used to 'home' the spacecraft on the Agena, and to control the Agena from the spacecraft prior to docking. The target vehicle had its own propulsion system and could be manoeuvred either from the spacecraft or the ground.

If the small end of Gemini had entered the Agena docking collar successfully, clamps inside the collar should grab the Gemini cone and pull it into a latched position. If the match had not started perfectly, the design was such that both craft should turn slightly and conform. If the Agena was bumped away the astronauts would merely set up for another attempt.

Six hours and thirty-four minutes into the mission the world's first docking between two spacecraft was safely accomplished. Not only was this a physical attachment between two vehicles, of the kind anticipated between spacecraft in the Apollo Moon programme, but in the same action control systems were automatically coupled. Thus the Gemini astronauts could start up Agena's 16,000-lb thrust engine and perform manœuvres as a combined spacecraft. The engine could then be used to make extensive orbital manœuvres.

It was some 20 min. after the vehicles had docked that troubles arose in dramatic fashion. Armstrong had fed. commands to the Agena and successfully accomplished a yaw manœuvre when the combined vehicle began to develop a fast rate of yaw and tumble. As it turned out this was caused by the uncommanded firing of one of Gemini's 25-lb roll thrusters. Armstrong separated from the Agena and after some difficulty turned the thruster off; control was regained by applying bursts of thrust from the re-entry attitude control system. When the spacecraft was finally brought under control it was found that nearly 75 per cent of the re-entry system's fuel supply had been used up, and ground control sent instructions to terminate the mission.

The emergency re-entry resulted in a landing on 16 March at 2223.08hr. EST 691 miles south-east of Okinawa. This was within 3 miles of the planned landing position. Armstrong and Scott emerged from the spacecraft about an hour after splash-down and awaited rescue in their inflatable raft. They were picked up by the destroyer USS *Mason* at 0138 hr. next morning.

Instead of the scheduled 3 days the flight had lasted 10 hr. 42 min. 6 sec., covering a distance of 181,450 miles and completing 7 revolutions of the Earth.

McDonnell traced the fault in Gemini 8 to a short-circuit in the electrical system affecting operation of the solenoid which opened the fuel and oxidizer valve in the thruster.

Owing to the curtailed flight programme only a small amount of data was received from 3 experiments, and Scott's 'space-walk' could not take place. Apart from using a hand-held gas-gun to control his movements, he was expected to experiment with a 'torqueless tool', loosening and tightening bolts on a work panel on the outside of the spacecraft's adapter module. The experiment was related to the problems of repair and assembly of large space structures in orbit. This important evaluation had to wait for another occasion.

Meanwhile, ground control repositioned the Agena target vehicle into a higher orbit so that it could be visited on a later mission. It carried a small micrometeoroid impact detector which Scott had intended to retrieve.

The last four Gemini missions were designed to develop routine rendezvous and docking manoeuvres, to demonstrate the ability of astronauts to perform simple work-tasks outside their craft, and generally to develop techniques ready for the sub-sequent three-man Apollo spacecraft. The first development versions of the Apollo command and service modules were already being launched from Cape Kennedy, unmanned, by the Uprated Saturn 1.

With Gemini 9 it was planned to make three rendezvous and docking tests with an Agena target vehicle and also to perform an EVA experiment lasting a total of 2 hr. 25 min. The latter was mainly to test an Astronaut Manoeuvring Unit (AMU) fixed to the astronaut's back.

The first disappointment came on 17 May 1966, when an Atlas carrying an Agena target vehicle developed a control system fault and fell into the Atlantic. Once again a Gemini launching had to be postponed until another target vehicle could be prepared; and this time a 1,700-lb Augmented Target Docking Adapter (ATDA) stood in for the Agena.

The ATDA, specially developed by McDonnell for such an emergency, had a similar docking collar as Agena but did not embody a rocket engine for powered manoeuvres. Nor did it have the micrometeoroid impact package as mounted on the Agena.

All went well with the launching of the ATDA on 1 June 1966, until telemetry reported that the nose-fairing had failed to eject. Nevertheless, it was orbiting successfully 186 miles above the Earth at the prescribed 28·9° inclination.

Then came a second frustration. An attempt to launch Gemini 9 some 100 min. later had to be abandoned because of a fault in ground data transmission affecting the rendezvous operation.

Astronauts Thomas P. Stafford and Eugene A. Cernan had to wait another 48 hr. for their mission to begin. This time, however, there were no 'technical holds' and on 3 June the rocket made a smooth departure at 0839.33 hr. EST to reach an orbit which ranged between 99 and 168 miles.

Orbiting in the same plane as the ATDA, there were no difficulties in achieving rendezvous which was completed during the third orbit. The astronauts then could appreciate the problem with the nose-fairing with their own eyes; it was hanging open 'like the jaws of an alligator' and shrouding the docking collar which Gemini was meant to engage.

Although Cernan was due to perform his first EVA experiment there was no suggestion that he should transfer to the vehicle and attempt to release the fairing.

Close inspection clearly showed that explosive bolts holding the fairing clamp ring had fired. However, the fairing was actually held not by the clamp but by wiring to the bolt firing squibs. The astronauts were able to make a full inspection from a distance of a few feet, reporting their findings to the ground. It appears that lanyards meant to disengage wiring quick-release plugs had not been properly attached prior to launching.

The flight plan was therefore revised to demonstrate two re-rendezvous manœuvres during the first day without the use of radar. These tests also simulated emergency docking manœuvres in which an Apollo Lunar Module (in this case Gemini) had to dock from a position above the target vehicle.

It was on the second day – on the thirty-first revolution – that Cernan began his EVA mission. His period of stay outside the spacecraft lasted 2 hr. 9 min., six times longer than White's. Much to his surprise, however, he found his work programme too demanding. After manœuvring on the end of the tether, and performing other exercises, he had some difficulty in maintaining orientation; and when at length he went to the back of the spacecraft to put on the AMU back pack the exertion caused the suit temperature to rise and his helmet visor to fog. At this stage Cernan was having difficulty opening one of the arm rests of the AMU, and the astronaut was promptly instructed to return to the cabin.

Cernan, in company with other astronauts, had previously made a number of successful flights with the AMU in the cabin of a specially padded transport aircraft flown to induce weightlessness. The 166-lb unit, fitted into the back of Gemini's adapter module, required Cernan, wearing a 42-lb chest pack with a 25-ft umbilical tether, to ease his back into its form-fitting seat with the help of special hand rails on the spacecraft, and open the arm rests. He was then to detach the pack and launch himself into space, having first fixed a 100-ft extension to the tether.

The AMU, developed by Ling-Temco-Vought, was 32 in. high, 22 in. wide and 19 in. deep. Attached to the astronaut it had self-contained systems providing for life-support, communications, telemetry, propulsion, and manual and automatic stabilization. Its hydrogen peroxide propulsion system included twelve small nozzles mounted in the corners of the back pack which the astronaut worked by manipulating controls on the arm rests. The jets were designed to give him complete freedom of movement in space, forwards, backwards, and sideways.

The flight of Gemini 9 continued for the full 3 days, and on 6 June the craft made a perfectly controlled semi-ballistic re-entry, to land only 0·4 mile from the planned landing point some 345 miles east of Bermuda. In completing 46 revolutions of the Earth, the craft had travelled 1,255,630 miles.

The next Gemini mission was a complete proof of astronauts' ability to handle their craft in routine space missions, for it involved nothing less than a rendezvous with two orbiting vehicles. This included the Agena spacecraft which had been left in a parking orbit some 300 miles above the Earth since the curtailed Gemini 8 mission of 16 March.

A new Agena climbed successfully into orbit on the afternoon of 18 July, to be followed some 100 min. later by Gemini 10 with astronauts John W. Young and Michael Collins. The manned craft lifted off at 1720.26 hr. EST, its Titan booster placing it into an initial orbit of 100–167 miles. Rendezvous with the Agena at 185 miles altitude proceeded according to programme and after the two vehicles had successfully docked preparations were made to start the second manœuvre which would place the combined spacecraft in a transfer orbit reaching that of the Agena which had been in space four months. Collins's task was to climb out and retrieve the meteoroid collector pack. Use was made of the attached Agena's propulsion system to modify the orbit, and after disengaging their craft the astronauts manœuvred alongside the target vehicle.

After the cabin had been depressurized Collins emerged on the end of a 25-ft tether while Young held the spacecraft only a few feet away from the Agena. Collins floated across to the vehicle, removed the meteoroid collector, and after 30 min. returned to the Gemini cabin. It was the first time that any man had made direct personal contact with another orbiting object.

Once again 3 days were spent in space. The splash-down came at 1606.11 hr. EST on 21 July at a point 530 miles due east of Cape Kennedy, just 3 miles from the planned position. The craft completed 44 revolutions, covering a distance of 1,223,370 miles.

The next objective in the Gemini programme was to tie two spacecraft together in orbit so that experiments could be made in passive attitude stabilization. This was the task of Gemini 11 astronauts Charles Conrad, Jr and Richard F. Gordon, Jr whose vehicle left the launch pad at 0942.26 hr. EST on 12 September 1966. The spacecraft's initial orbit ranged between 100 and 177 miles, and as on previous occasions, an Agena target vehicle had gone up some 100 min. before. The object was a rendezvous during Gemini's first revolution of the Earth; also known as direct-ascent rendezvous, this was successfully achieved some 94 min. after lift-off. The astronauts used their on-board computer and radar equipment with only minimal assistance from ground tracking stations.

After the vehicles had docked, Gemini 11 used Agena's restartable rocket engine to extend the orbit in a wide ellipse ranging between 179 and 850 miles. Maximum speed in this orbit was calculated to be 17,967 m.p.h. Some of the most striking colour photographs of the Earth were taken on this mission, particularly views of India and Ceylon from 529 miles altitude and the north-west of Australia from near the orbital zenith.

These and other Gemini pictures placed geography in a new perspective and were closely studied by scientists concerned with cartography, geology, and oceanography for the wealth of detail they contained. So clear was one photograph taken over North Africa, on the second day of the flight, that a small black 'fuzz' on the Saudi Arabian desert was later identified as smoke from a fire which occurred at a crude-oil pipeline.

The astronauts docked and undocked four times with their Agena target and still had sufficient fuel left to make another unplanned rendezvous with the Agena.

After the cabin had been depressurized Gordon stood up for 2 hr. 8 min. with his head and shoulders projecting through the open hatch to photograph stars, clouds, and the Earth under different conditions of lighting.

The other period of EVA, planned to last 2 hr., had to be cut short. The craft were now back in a near-circular orbit at 184 miles and the astronaut's main task – during the thirty-first revolution – was to hook a 100-ft Dacron tether between the docked Agena and the docking bar on his own craft. The tether was stored in the Agena near the docking collar. Although the connexion was achieved, Gordon was perspiring so heavily that moisture clouded his vision and overloaded the environmental control system of his pressure suit. He returned to the cabin after 44 min.

This was the second time that an EVA experiment had had to be cut short because of excessive astronaut exertions. To fix the tether Gordon had been forced to clamp his legs round the small end of Gemini in order to work in the weightless environment with two hands.

After the cabin had been resealed and the oxygen atmosphere restored to 5 p.s.i. pressure, Gemini 11 was separated from the Agena and the tether pulled taut, thus demonstrating how clusters of spacecraft might be fastened together in space to prevent them drifting apart. It also helped to assess a method of stabilizing vehicles towards the Earth by purely passive means, using the Earth's gravitational gradient.

The astronauts also showed how two spacecraft joined by a tether could be made to rotate round their common centre of mass to simulate gravity by centrifugal force. The crew fired Gemini's thrusters so that the craft began a cartwheel motion; and for the first time in space, a trace of artificial gravity was generated – about ·00015 of normal Earth gravity – inside the Gemini cabin. This was a demonstration in miniature of the kind of technique that may have to be adopted in large space-stations of the future.

Despite the shortened 'space-walk', the mission was regarded as highly successful, and in returning to Earth the craft made the first automatic controlled computer-steered re-entry of a manned spacecraft. This was one of the most accurate Gemini landings. The craft splashed down 701 miles east of Miami, Florida, at 0859·34 hr. EST on 15 September only 1·5 miles from the planned position. It had travelled a total distance of 1,232,530 miles.

The last of the Gemini series was intended to clear up outstanding problems, particularly those affecting the ability of an astronaut to work outside his orbiting spacecraft. NASA had, in fact, entirely re-written the EVA programme in the light of prevailing difficulties which meant abandoning a second planned experiment with an AMU.

Gemini 12 was launched at 1546.33 hr. EST on 11 November 1966, 98 min. after its Agena target vehicle. The initial orbit ranged between 100 and 175 miles. Astronauts James Lovell and Edwin Aldrin made contact with Agena at 185 miles as planned and docked with it on their third orbit. A defect in Agena's primary propulsion system prevented a planned manoeuvre into a 185–460-mile orbit. However, a retrograde burn of 43 ft/sec., using Agena's secondary propulsion system, changed the orbit of the combined vehicles to 160–177 miles, setting the orbit to phase with the 12 November total eclipse of the Sun over South America. Following a sleep period, there was another eclipse-phasing manœuvre which enabled the crew, through the Gemini windows, to obtain the first solar eclipse photographs from space.

The next task on that day was for Aldrin, the EVA astronaut, to take photographs of the Earth and stars with the cabin de-pressurized and the hatch open – as Cernan had done before his 'space-walk'. He had also to fix a portable hand rail on the out-side of the craft. The hatch was open 2 hr. 29 min.

The big test was reserved for the third day. Aldrin climbed out of the cabin trailing a 30-ft umbilical tether. Using the hand rail previously mounted, he worked his way to the docked Agena. A pair of nylon body tethers, adjustable from 1·5 to 3 ft, were then fastened by means of pip pins inserted into holes at various points on the small end of Gemini and into rings on each side of the astronaut's parachute harness. After resting Aldrin was then able to perform his appointed tasks with little effort, pulling out the end of the 100-ft Dacron tether from the stowage near Agena's docking collar and looping the end over Gemini's docking bar. He also exposed a micrometeoroid collector plate on the Agena.

Later, the astronaut was to transfer to the spacecraft's adapter module, locating his feet in 'overshoe' restraints. After another rest period he began a 'work task evaluation' at a 30 in. by 30 in. panel on which were mounted electrical and fluid connexions, combinations of hooks and rings, strips of Velcro, and fixed and removable bolts. First he worked – loosening and tightening bolts, plugging and unplugging sockets – using only the foot restraints and then with only the body tethers.

After this exercise Aldrin made his way back to the space-craft's nose to perform another sequence of work-tasks on a smaller panel, using the same body tethers as before to help con-trol his body position. Before working at each site he fixed a camera so that his subsequent actions could be fully recorded.

Aldrin took about a dozen 2-min. rest periods and making full use of restraint straps and hand-holds, he was far more successful than previous astronauts in resisting fatigue. His pressure suit did not overheat, and at no time did his heart rate exceed 130 per min. He remained outside the cabin for a record time of 2 hr. 29 min. 25 sec.

After Aldrin had returned the spacecraft were undocked and allowed to drift at random. The craft stabilized in vertical formation after 1 orbit, the tether exercise lasting a total of 4 hr. 17 min. Then, on the last day of the flight, Aldrin performed another 52 min. of open-hatch photography. This brought his total exposure to space during the three EVA periods to over 5 hr. 30 min.

The mission was rounded off by an accurate return on 15 November ending with a splash-down at 1421.04 hr. EST, 720 miles south-east of Cape Kennedy. The craft had covered 1,628,510 miles, making over 59 revolutions of the Earth. This landing only 2.7 miles from the aiming point brought an historic series of spaceflights to a worthy close. The entire spectacle, including landing, helicopter pick-up of the astronauts, and their enthusiastic welcome aboard the aircraft carrier *Wasp*, was televised live via the Early Bird satellite and relayed throughout the United States.

At a ceremony at his Texas ranch on 23 November, President Johnson presented the Gemini 12 astronauts with Exceptional Service Awards of the National Aeronautics and Space Administration. These acknowledged not only Lovell and Aldrin. They honoured all the astronauts (fifty were then in training), the check-out and launch crews; the flight controllers; the tracking station personnel; recovery forces, and the men and women who designed and built the spacecraft, the Titan, Atlas, and Agena rockets, and the vast array of supporting equipment.

The record was impressive. America was now far ahead of the Soviet Union in almost every aspect of manned spaceflight. In terms of distance travelled, Mercury and Gemini had logged 17,616,000 miles; Vostok and Voskhod 7,471,000 miles. But still more impressive was the fact that the two Powers combined had performed 25,000,000 miles of pioneering space travel apparently without loss or injury to any of the participants.

The bridge to the Moon was fast being erected, and the Apollo programme upon which all effort now concentrated seemed capable of achieving John Kennedy's goal of placing American astronauts on the lunar surface by 1970.

The stage had been reached when three Apollo spacecraft had been launched unmanned by the Uprated Saturn 1 substituting for the larger Saturn 5 of the actual Moon programme. The first unmanned Apollo sub-orbital launching, on 26 February 1966, was mainly to prove re-entry characteristics of the command module and by the end of the year NASA was approaching the stage where the first Apollo command and service modules would be tested with a three-man crew in Earth-orbit. The flight, scheduled to begin on 21 February 1967, was expected to last a maximum of 14 days.

The first spacecraft disaster, when it struck, therefore was all the more stunning for happening not in space but on the ground. It removed from the family of space pioneers three brave men, two of whom had already made space history. They were Virgil Grissom, the Apollo command pilot, who had previously made space flights in 1961 and 1965, and Edward White, the first American to leave a spacecraft in orbit; the third was Roger Chaffee who had yet to make his mark in space.

The disaster occurred on Launch Complex 34 at Cape Kennedy as the astronauts were participating in a practice countdown in readiness for the first manned orbital flight aboard the Apollo 204 spacecraft. The command and service modules were mounted in the nose of the Uprated Saturn 1 launch vehicle, which was unfuelled, and the astronauts in their cabin had already been there over 5 hr. The service tower was in place round the vehicle and at the time of the tragedy the spacecraft was operating on external power.

The first warning of fire came at 1831.04 hr. EST while the countdown was holding at T— 10 min. (i.e. 10 min. from the time of simulated lift-off). Up to this point NASA reported only minor difficulties with the equipment, the reason for the 'hold' being

to provide an opportunity to improve communications between
the spacecraft and the ground crew. Cabin pressure, cabin
temperature, and oxygen suit supply temperature were normal.
Cabin pressure in the pure oxygen environment was about 16
p.s.i. before the fire – a value necessary at ground-level to achieve
the desired pressure balance, but which in an actual launching
would be reduced to about 5 p.s.i. as the craft climbed into
space.

The fire appeared to start unseen at the lower left of the capsule below the feet of astronaut Grissom. The investigating
Board thought it possible that a 'hot wire' or short-circuit
initiated a fire that spread to nylon netting (used to prevent loose
objects from floating into equipment crevices while in zero-g),
Velcro fastening material (used to attach equipment to the cabin
interior), and the environmental control unit insulation.

It took some 15 sec. from the first report of fire (by Chaffee)
until the cabin shell burnt through between the inner and outer
hulls. Pressure inside the capsule immediately prior to this was
36 p.s.i. All three suits burned through, Grissom's (on the extreme
left of the cabin) receiving the greatest exposure to flame and
Chaffee's (on the opposite side) the least. Yet the fire had surprising variability in intensity and timing. Dr Robert C. Seamans,
Jr, Deputy Administrator of NASA, cited the example of an
aluminium tubing handle which had a hole burned through it,
indicating a temperature at that point of at least 760°C, yet its
nylon hinge within 2 in. of the melted spot was relatively undamaged indicating a temperature there of less than 254°C.

Dr Seamans reported:

> One hypothesis, supported by the cabin pressure history,
> assumes a small, low-grade fire whose heat was at first
> largely absorbed by the spacecraft structure and that was
> burning at the time of the first crew report; that fire may
> have continued for as long as 10 sec. A more intense fire may
> have developed, causing the rapid increase in cabin pressure.
> This fire was probably then extinguished by the depletion of
> oxygen.

Death was attributed to asphyxiation caused by inhalation of smoke.

Grissom had recorded an epitaph for himself and his fellow-astronauts in an interview which followed his epic mission in Gemini 3: 'If we die,' he said, 'we want people to accept it. We are in a risky business and we hope that if anything happens to us it will not delay the programme. The conquest of space is worth the risk of life.'

Almost immediately NASA announced the names of the replacement crew: Captain Walter M. Schirra, Jr, command pilot; Major Donn F. Eisele, senior pilot; and Major Walter Cunningham, pilot. This was the back-up team whose training had paralleled that of the dead astronauts. Later, when the extent of the modifications required to ensure safety of the Apollo space-craft was fully realized, active training of crews for Apollo missions was temporarily suspended and the astronauts pre-viously chosen to make them (including the reserve crew of AS-204) were stood down. It was some time before American astronauts were ready to go into space again.

Thus began the era of human exploration of the Moon, on the wings of both triumph and tragedy.*

---

* Two trainee astronauts, the former test-pilot Elliot M. See, Jr., and Captain Charles Bassett of the US Air Force, had been killed on 28 February 1966 when their T-38 Talon jet-trainer crashed into the McDonnell factory in St Louis. They were preparing for the three-day Gemini 9 mission subse-quently flown by Thomas Stafford and Eugene Cernan. Elliot See was to have been command pilot and Charles Bassett was being trained for a 90-minute 'space walk'. Another trainee astronaut, Theodore Freeman, was lost in 1964 when a goose smashed through the windscreen of his T-38.

CHAPTER THREE

THE LUNAR EXPLORERS

The spaceport for America's Apollo Moon programme was built
on a wasteland of sand and swamp adjacent to Cape Kennedy on
Merritt Island. To achieve it NASA spent 1,000,000,000 dollars
in what must be the biggest and most expensive construction
project of all time. The major facility, Launch Complex 39,
required 1,000,000 tons of steel and nearly 17,000,000 tons of
concrete. The site occupies 80,000 acres and is criss-crossed with
100 miles of roads and 22 miles of railways; and dominating the
skyline is one particular structure known as the VAB or Vertical
Assembly Building.

The VAB is the assembly hangar for Saturn 5 and its Apollo
spacecraft, and so gigantic are its proportions that no fewer than
four of these massive vehicle combinations can be vertically
assembled at the same time. Each assembly bay has work plat-
forms which can be extended vertically and horizontally to provide access to the vehicle at any level. Next door is the Launch
Control Center and a full simulated countdown can be carried
out while the vehicle is still inside the building. Nearly 600 ft
long, 418 ft high, and 410 ft wide, the building is so large that,
were it not for the special air-conditioning system, clouds could
form inside.

A lunar mission actually starts in the VAB for it is here that
the complete vehicle is assembled on a mobile launch pad and
fully checked-out ready for flight. After final inspection, a huge
door in the VAB is opened and the unfuelled 364-ft vehicle is
slowly moved out complete with launch pad and 380-ft umbilical
tower on a gigantic diesel-powered crawler-transporter. This
lethargic monster with its 12,000,000-lb load moves at only 1
mile per hr. along the crawlerway which leads to the launch
pads nearly 3 miles distant. At its destination are three launch
pads. Each has an elevated concrete and steel structure at its
centre which receives the pad-mounted vehicle and umbilical

tower on the mobile transporter after it has negotiated a ramp.

After the rocket and its mobile launch pad are in position on the support pedestal, technicians gain access to the vehicle by means of hinged walkways which extend from the umbilical tower. A 400-ft mobile service tower is also moved into position close to the rocket. Basic systems are now re-checked and a number of vital interconnexions made between launch pad and vehicle. At length the spacecraft is fuelled. Tanking the rocket with kerosene (RP-1), liquid oxygen and liquid hydrogen occurs last. Finally, the flame deflector is moved into position on rails in the trench beneath the launch pedestal. Its mobility allows use of a second flame deflector when the first is being refurbished after a firing.

The three astronauts, of course, participate in the last hours of the check procedure. Just before launching, the service tower is moved back while the umbilical tower is left in position. As the countdown reaches its climax the five powerful F-1 engines in the first stage ignite, and ponderously the 6,000,000-lb space leviathan lifts from the pad. The engines are consuming kerosene and liquid oxygen at the prodigious rate of 5,000 gallons per sec.; thrust is 7,500,000 lb. The noise is deafening.

In the Launch Control Center 3 miles away a vast array of electronic monitoring equipment registers every vital part of the launch procedure as technicians watch the lift-off on television screens.

In the first 2 min. the rocket burns 2,100 tons of propellant. After the vehicle has made its programmed turn over the Atlantic Ocean, and is climbing at a height of some 30 miles, the S-IC first stage jettisons leaving the S-II stage to continue propulsion. At 2.54 min. from lift-off, the launch escape system is jettisoned. When the vehicle has reached 100 miles some 9.04 min. into the flight, the second stage falls away; and the S-IVB third stage begins thrusting to place the spacecraft into a parking orbit close to the Earth. Speed is 17,500 m.p.h.; elapsed time 11 min. 52 sec.

This is Apollo's first 'breathing-space' in the flight programme, and the time when systems are re-checked in conjunction with ground control. At NASA's Manned Spacecraft Center at

Houston, Texas, computers will calculate Apollo's orbit and determine the time when the S-IVB's engines must be restarted to enter the spacecraft on the desired transfer orbit to the Moon.

If all is well, at the appointed time, the third-stage engine re-fires and the astronauts prepare for the next vital stage of their lunar journey. If translunar injection is made on the second orbit, the time into the mission will be just over 3 hr. The speed at which engine cut-off occurs is critical. It must be between 35,000 and 36,500 ft/sec.

Soon after the vehicle has entered the coast phase of the mission preparations are made to start the transposition and docking manœuvre which prepares the craft for the subsequent lunar landing procedure.

This entails separating the command and service modules from the expended S-IVB rocket stage and blowing free the adapter panels which shroud the lunar module carried in this rear compartment. The manœuvre is completed by flying the command and service modules out a short distance ahead, turning them through 180° by use of gas-jet controls, and gently bringing them back so that the docking mechanism on the nose of the command module enters the docking drogue of the lunar module attached to the S-IVB.

With this achieved the lunar module is pulled away from the rocket stage which is left behind.

Mid-course corrections are now carried out to align the trajectory accurately with the Moon which itself is moving relative to the Earth at about 2,300 m.p.h. The spacecraft, of course, does not maintain a uniform speed as it coasts towards the Moon; speed varies constantly under the influence of gravitation, averaging about 5,500 m.p.h.

To ensure accuracy and timing, the necessary velocity adjustments are computed on Earth and relayed to the spacecraft. Communications are maintained by a chain of stations round the world, including the NASA Deep Space Network Stations in the United States, Spain, South Africa, and Australia. As one station disappears below the horizon on the rotating Earth, another has appeared to keep the link open. The DSN Stations have highly directional 85-ft dish antennae providing a range accuracy of 49 ft at the distance of the Moon; they have been used regularly to receive data from space probes including television pictures of the lunar surface. The largest directional station at Goldstone has a 210-ft dish with a range two and a half times that of the other antennae; it is capable of following a spacecraft to the edge of the Solar System.

Mid-course corrections are made after Apollo has been orientated at the prescribed angle by firing the service module's rocket engine in an accurately controlled burst. In a typical mission as many as three velocity adjustments may be necessary. A first 'coarse' correction might be applied as early as 5 hr. 6 min. into the flight; a second smaller adjustment could be made at 55 hr. 30 min. and a third at 63 hr. 15 min.

During the 70 hr. of flight the astronauts have many tasks to perform working in 8-hr. shifts. They are in constant touch with Houston by radio and television.

Apollo carries fuel-cells for electrical power supply. Liquid hydrogen and oxygen flow from separate tanks into the fuel-cell battery, water being produced as a by-product. A similar system was used in long-duration Gemini missions. In Apollo the water is used for drinking and general cleansing purposes. Food includes the hydrated kind tested during the Gemini programme. Rest and sleep are taken at regular intervals and spacesuits can be doffed in the cabin's shirt-sleeve environment.

One of the principal tasks during the translunar journey is that of checking equipment in the lunar module. The action of docking has previously made a pressure-tight seal between the two vehicles. In order to pass freely between them, however, the astronauts must first open the hatch covers and remove the docking fixture. The interconnecting tunnel is then free of obstruction and transfer between them simply a matter of crawling through. The lunar module will, of course, be pressurized at the same value as the command module. The astronauts emerge into the lunar module through a hatch in the roof of the compartment aft of the control cabin. After ensuring that everything is in order they rejoin their companion in the command module.

After the final mid-course correction the Moon will be looming large in the sky exerting increasing gravitational pull and tending to speed up the vehicles. Again computers on Earth will monitor equipment on board the spacecraft to ensure that the trajectory is exactly right to achieve a 'miss' of 90 to 100 miles. The spacecraft will be approaching the Moon in a backward attitude, the large nozzle of its service module facing forward in the path of flight. To place the craft into orbit round the Moon, this engine must be used as a retro-rocket to slow down the vehicles near the point of closest approach. Elapsed time at the point of retro-fire could be approximately 64 hr. 15 min.

When retro-thrust has been applied, the combined craft should begin to swing into orbit round the Moon some 90 miles above its surface. The astronauts now look down upon the vast airless panorama of dry lava 'seas', craters, and mountains, already familiar from the reconnaissance pictures taken by unmanned Ranger, Orbiter, and Luna space probes. Sunlight floods the surface casting intense black shadows. In the absence of a protective blanket of air, meteoroids and radiation at all frequencies bombard the surface.

When the Sun is directly overhead temperatures can exceed 100°C. A lunar day and a lunar night are approximately 14 Earth days long, and as the night shadow slowly creeps across the Moon's face, in the absence of an absorbing atmosphere, there is a sudden fall to around −160°C.

The spacecraft, orbiting at about 3,500 m.p.h., will complete 1 revolution of the Moon every 2 hr. During the first part of the orbit the astronauts make an equipment check, sight landmarks for orbit determination, and update the guidance navigation and control sub-systems. Now final preparations can be made for the task of landing the lunar module at the appointed site near the lunar equator.

After transferring to the lunar module, the commander and systems engineer check all vital equipment including propulsion, guidance control, and 'abort' systems. Communication with Earth is possible when the vehicle has emerged from behind the

Moon which will otherwise block the reception of radio signals. If everything is in order the 'go' signal is received from the Manned Spacecraft Center in Houston, and the landing procedure begun.

The commander of the lunar module and the systems engineer take up their positions in the lunar module. They do not have seats or crew couches, but stand at the control consoles secured by restraint harnesses.

Two actions remain to be performed before casting off. One is to extend the landing legs of the lunar module. Another is to replace the docking mechanism in the nose of the command module ready for the return lunar-orbit rendezvous and docking. The hatches to the interconnecting tunnel in both vehicles must also be closed to form gas-tight seals.

After the astronauts have brought all systems to operational readiness and assuming there are no snags, they undock the landing craft from the Apollo parent. The two vehicles moving in close formation above the Moon are in touch by radio, and before starting the descent the lunar module astronauts conduct test-manœuvres to ensure that the thrusters of the Reaction Control Sub-system (RCS) are in working order. Each phase of the test procedure is monitored by the third crew-member (navigator), who remains behind in the parent vehicle.

The landing will be made ideally within a few hundred yards of the chosen site, based on accurate maps prepared from the thousands of close-up photographs obtained principally by Lunar Orbiter probes. Once again orbital parameters necessary to ensure an accurate descent trajectory will be computed on Earth and stored in the spacecraft.

With the lunar module correctly orientated for retro-fire, its rocket engine reduces speed sufficiently for the vehicle to enter an elliptical orbit. If no further action were taken this would cause it to swing within 50,000 ft of the Moon's surface before returning to the original apogee on the opposite side of the Moon.

However, if all proceeds normally, the point of closest approach will be approximately 225 miles uprange of the proposed landing site.

As the lunar module's elliptical orbit has a period similar to that of the parent vehicle, the two craft will remain in line-of-sight communication and the approach path of the landing craft can be verified by mutual radar tracking from both vehicles.

Retro-fire for landing normally begins at the time of closest approach, using near-maximum thrust along a minimum-energy trajectory. Engine thrust is variable between 8,200 and 1,100 lb. Owing to the high pitch angles required for the braking manœuvre, however, the landing site is not immediately visible to the astronauts and the descent is performed automatically to within 700 ft of the surface. The manœuvre proceeds in three stages. First the *braking phase* from approximately 50,000 to 10,000 ft; second a *final approach phase* from approximately 10,000 to 700 ft, and third the *landing phase* which terminates at touchdown.

The lunar module is orientated ready for the final approach phase some 2 min. before reaching the 10,000 ft mark and then the astronauts have an unobstructed forward view. At this time new data can be fed into the guidance system to select an alternative landing site if the approach path to the primary area is not exactly right.

Once rocket thrust counterbalances the spacecraft's weight (now approximately $\frac{1}{6}$th of the Earth value), the vehicle is able to hover, ascend, or move sideways in the low-gravity environment. Even at this stage, if anything is wrong, the mission can be 'aborted' by firing off the ascent stage of the spacecraft which forms an escape capsule capable of returning to lunar orbit. However, if all is well, the craft can continue in the hovering-drift mode for up to 2 min. while the astronauts, peering down at the lunar surface through their windows, choose a suitably smooth landing place. Although the craft can land entirely automatically using a radio-altimeter to gauge height, small rocks or other obstructions are best judged by the astronauts themselves. The standard procedure, therefore, is for the landing to be performed by the command pilot. The method of manual control is similar to that of a helicopter. The astronaut works a translation controller with the left hand and an attitude controller with the right. Control actions, transmitted electrically, work valves in the Reaction Control Sub-system which release propellant to the thrusters in appropriate measure; for example, tilting the vehicle in the hover mode produces forward or backward translation.

The procedure will have been well rehearsed on Earth where the astronauts will have learnt to control jet-powered simulators. The shadow cast by the spacecraft itself is a useful gauge of height over the surface and when this is down to 3 ft, engine thrust is cut and the vehicle drops to rest on the landing legs.

With landing safely accomplished, the first task will be to check all systems in readiness for the return take-off, for if anything is wrong the maximum time must be allowed for rectification. A major engine fault could leave the astronauts stranded on the Moon. A full report is made both to the third astronaut in lunar orbit on VHF and directly to Earth using S-band frequencies (employed in Apollo for purposes of both tracking and communications). This decides if the planned stay-time can be accomplished.

With check-out completed the exploration phase begins. It is a rule that only one astronaut at a time emerges from the ship; the other remains inside to monitor operations and maintain communications. Beneath his EVA pressure suit the lunar explorer wears next to the skin a water-cooled undergarment which serves to control internal temperature. On his back is fitted a portable life-support system, which supplies cool purified oxygen to the suit at 4·8 to 5·2 p.s.i. On top goes a thermally insulated coverall shrouding helmet and life-support pack. There are also special gloves and thick-soled insulated boots.

To leave the craft the lunar module's cabin is depressurized while both astronauts retain suit pressure. The forward hatch beneath the centre instrument consoles is opened and the explorer-astronaut climbs out using the platform and stairway that extend from the side. The lunar module is then repressurized.

First task for the man outside is to inspect the craft for damage such as might be caused by small rocks thrown up by the engine exhaust. Next he extends the S-band antenna so that photographs from a small hand-held television camera can be sent back to Earth via the S-band link.

The portable life-support system allows the astronaut to work for periods of up to 3 hr. Apart from taking photographs, he will collect samples of lunar rock and make observations and measurements of the lunar topography. All the time he will be in direct visual and voice contact, over VHF, with his companion in the lunar module.

After his time of exploration is over, the craft is depressurized and the astronaut climbs back inside. The hatch is closed and pressure restored. Cabin repressurization takes about 1 min.

The portable life-support system is now replenished while voice reports are transmitted to Earth together with scientific data. Another excursion outside the craft can now be made by the second astronaut using the same procedure.

Scientific experiments, of course, are an important feature of the exploration programme. To facilitate this effort NASA provides Apollo Lunar Surface Experiments Package (ALSEP) payloads, which are entirely self-contained ready for the astronaut to remove from a compartment in the descent stage between two of the landing legs (see pages 224–5).

As sunlight to power solar cells will not be available during the lunar night, and large quantities of chemical energy would be required for long-term fuel-cell operation, ALSEP packages are powered by a SNAP-27* thermoelectric nuclear generator. Using plutonium-238 as the heat source the unit supplies 56 W of electricity for 1 year.

Fuelling the generator is a task in itself. The plutonium fuel is carried in a storage cask separately attached to the side of the descent module.† First the astronaut removes the two ALSEP packages and the inert SNAP-27 generator. To fuel the generator the astronaut first hinges the storage cask into a horizontal

---

* SNAP is the contraction of Systems of Nuclear Auxiliary Power.

† This mounting arrangement is necessary in order to prevent the radio-isotope fuel from dispersing on the Earth in the event of a launch mishap. The storage cask, held by metal bands, has a heat shield and is designed to re-enter as a stable atmospheric vehicle.

position and extracts the fuel capsule with a special handling tool. With the same tool he inserts the capsule vertically into the generator housing and locks it in position.

The two ALSEP packages are then assembled on a bar and carried by the astronaut to the desired location. There is no difficulty in transporting the system over several hundred feet since the 180-lb load under lunar gravity conditions is only about 30 lb. It is important to set the equipment some distance from the lunar module to avoid possible damage from flying debris as the vehicle takes off.

At the experiment site the generator and scientific equipment, linked by cables to a telemetry transmitter, are laid out around a central platform. Apart from serving as a junction-box for the wiring, the platform carries the helical telemetry antenna which is gimbal-mounted at the top of a short mast. To achieve the desired signal strength at the receiving station the antenna must be carefully aimed at the Earth.

After the astronaut has activated the instruments they should continue to supply data from the lunar surface for 6 months to a year.

The first seven ALSEP experiments planned by NASA were as follows:

1. *Passive Lunar Seismic Experiment.* A 3-axis seismometer measures lunar tremors or 'moonquakes' allowing study of the Moon's interior to its centre, i.e. whether it has a crust and core and whether it is layered in structure.

2. *Lunar Tri-Axis Magnetometer.* This instrument, similar to ones flown in unmanned spacecraft, measures the Moon's internal magnetic field as well as the interaction of the solar wind with the magnetic field round the Moon.

3. *Medium Energy Solar Wind Experiment.* A plasma spectrometer measures the velocity and direction of protons, electrons, and alpha-particles in the solar wind as they arrive at the Moon and the interaction of these particles with the lunar surface.

4. *Suprathermal Ion Detector.* This experiment measures the Moon's ionosphere by sampling ions in a wide range of energies to determine how strongly it is affected by the solar wind.

5. *Lunar Heat Flow Measurements.* This instrument measures the outflow of heat from the Moon's interior through the surface to provide information on the distribution of radioactive elements and the thermal history of the Moon, including volcanism.

6. *Low Energy Solar Wind.* As in the case of experiment 3, this instrument studies solar wind particles, but in the lower energy ranges.

7. *Active Lunar Seismic Experiment.* After the instrument is activated, an astronaut hits the lunar surface with a thumping device as he walks out to 1,000 ft from the lunar module. Beyond that distance, a small mortar device is used to fire small projectiles to land on the surface; the instrument measures the local tremors to obtain information on physical properties of the lunar crust to a depth of about 5,000 ft.

Following the period of lunar exploration, which initially lasts about 24 hr., the astronauts seal the hatch of the lunar module for the last time and repressurize the cabin. All systems are brought to operational status and the vehicle's launch readiness confirmed to Apollo Control on Earth and also to the astronaut orbiting in the parent spacecraft.

The launch method, originally developed in feasibility studies by the British Interplanetary Society between 1938 and 1947, involves using the spacecraft's leg-supported descent stage as the launch platform. Not only does this provide a stable platform for the lift-off but leaving the base section behind considerably reduces the deadweight to be lifted into lunar orbit.

The ascent path must be precisely matched with the orbit azimuth and approach time of the parent spacecraft. The situation recalls the prior work with Gemini and Agena in which the aim was to rendezvous during the first orbit. Acting on computed data stored in the lunar module, the astronauts can have manual control over engine ignition or programmed command.

Lift-off will follow a countdown when the vehicle is approaching in line of sight over the horizon. The ascent stage rises on a thrust of 3,500 lb, its engine burning continuously up to the point of insertion into the transfer orbit which will bring it to the rendezvous position. During the first 12 sec. the craft rises vertically; then follow two 'pitchover' phases, the first steeper than the second. The engine is cut at a height of some 50,000 ft approximately 7 min. after lift-off. At this point the vehicle is in an ascent transfer orbit, which nominally intercepts the Apollo parent at the first intersection of the two vehicles' orbits.

If, for any reason, lift-off of the lunar module is delayed for more than 1·5 min., the craft must 'loiter' in the 50,000-ft altitude parking orbit before a second engine firing is made to insert the craft into a revised orbit for rendezvous. Lift-off from the Moon cannot be left longer than 8 min. as in this time the parent vehicle will have disappeared below the Moon's horizon. In this event, the astronauts must wait some 2 hr. for the next launch opportunity on the succeeding orbit.

However, if the craft has been successfully injected into the transfer orbit for rendezvous, it should approach the Apollo parent within 500 ft. The commander manually manœuvres the lunar module to a docking attitude and increases or decreases the rate of closure until docking is accomplished.

Although the parent vehicle normally remains passive during this operation, if necessary it can perform rendezvous and docking. In fact, should the lunar module fail to achieve rendezvous there are contingency plans whereby the Apollo parent will modify its orbit to 'chase' the smaller craft and dock with it. Reserve propellant is carried for this purpose.

With docking completed the two astronauts prepare to rejoin their companion in the command module. Pressures between the two craft are equalized, systems of the ascent stage turned off, and after removal of the docking mechanism in the interconnecting tunnel, scientific equipment and lunar samples are transferred to the parent vehicle.

With the three astronauts reunited, the docking fixture is left in the lunar module, and the cabin hatch resealed. The lunar module is then jettisoned.

After more equipment checks, preparations are made to restart the engine of the Apollo service module for the return flight. Once again the transfer orbit and launch timing are computed on Earth and stored in the spacecraft. At the appropriate moment the 200,000-lb thrust J-2 engine fires, propelling the craft to a speed of about 5,600 m.p.h. to achieve escape from the Moon. The return journey lasts approximately 60 hr. As Apollo approaches the Earth, speed will increase to about 25,000 m.p.h. because of the Earth's gravitational pull.

Ground stations again supply data for mid-course manœuvres, for accuracy of the trans-earth trajectory is vital to the astronauts' safe return. Communications are assisted by the Atlantic satellite in geo-stationary orbit, which passes signals received from the spacecraft between the NASA ground station on Ascension Island and the United States as the vehicle heads towards its destination.

The approach trajectory must hit a re-entry corridor only 26 miles wide. Otherwise the vehicle will be in danger of missing the Earth and being deflected into a remote part of space. On the other hand, dipping too steeply into the Earth's atmosphere could mean destruction of the spacecraft by excessive frictional heating.

Thus, the mid-course manœuvres must be carried out with exceptional accuracy. Then, with the vehicle on target, and about 15 min. before entry into the Earth's atmosphere, the service module is jettisoned. This leaves the conical command module to make the final descent.

Using pitch control jets the spacecraft commander turns the vehicle over so that the blunt heat shield faces forward to absorb re-entry heating. There are no retro-rockets to brake the speed. As the craft cuts through the atmosphere temperatures on the shield's surface can reach 2742°C.

It is not entirely a ballistic return. The command module, with its offset centre of gravity, can produce a certain amount of aerodynamic lift. The ablative material protecting the craft is thickened on one side to provide for this. In this way the commander can manœuvre the capsule to stay in the narrow re-entry corridor and select his landing point. He can, in fact, guide the craft to a selected landing area at sea as far as 5,000 miles away.

By the time the craft has dropped to within 30,000 ft, drag-braking has reduced the speed to around sonic velocity. At 25,000 ft, drogue parachutes are deployed, followed at 15,000 ft by three huge ringsail landing parachutes which lower the capsule gently into the sea. As the craft splashes down the parachutes are severed and the astronauts await helicopter rescue.

The samples they have brought from the Moon's surface, sealed into special containers, are taken to the Lunar Receiving Laboratory at the NASA Manned Spacecraft Center in Houston. The material is quarantined, examined, and subsequently processed for detailed study and analysis by the world scientific community.

CHAPTER FOUR

SPACECRAFT IN FOCUS

Vostok (pages 17, 19, 20–6)

Certain technical features of the world's first manned spacecraft were kept secret for four years after the pioneer single orbit performed by Major (later Colonel) Yuri Gagarin on 12 April 1961. We now know that the spacecraft had two main sections, a spherical re-entry capsule of 7·5 ft diameter and an instrument compartment which included a retro-rocket system.

The capsule itself was comprehensively clad in an ablative material for protection of the cosmonaut against frictional heating and swathed in strips of metal foil as a means of reflecting solar heat in orbit. A rocket ejection seat for the cosmonaut slid into the capsule on rails, with access through a large circular hatch. The seat rails were inclined to the horizontal ensuring ejection of the cosmonaut at an upward angle. Exit from the vehicle was possible by blowing explosive studs securing the escape hatch immediately behind the cosmonaut's head.

Of the six cosmonauts who made orbital flights in Vostok spacecraft, Gagarin alone remained inside the capsule for the landing. Owing to the capsule's high sinking rate beneath its recovery parachute, the normal procedure was to eject at low altitude following re-entry for separate parachute recovery.

Whereas the American Mercury spacecraft was stabilized by gas-jets during re-entry, Vostok's spherical capsule had no such refinement. After the vehicle had been ejected from orbit by rocket braking, four tensioning bands holding the capsule to the instrument section were released. The latter, having served its function, was allowed to plunge into the atmosphere and burn up. Meanwhile, the spherical re-entry body containing the cosmonaut slowly assumed its correct attitude as it encountered the Earth's atmosphere.

Orientation was achieved by the simple procedure of weighting the capsule forward of the geometric centre so that, as air pressure built up, it slowly swung round into the correct re-entry attitude to take the brunt of frictional heating on the thickest part of the heat shield. In this attitude the cosmonaut, lying on his ejection seat, was subjected to re-entry deceleration 'chest-to-back' in the approved manner. It seems probable that early Soviet ballistic warheads were developed on this principle, creating confidence in the technique for manned experiments.

The world received a first glimpse of 'the Vostok spacecraft' at the Tushino Air Display in July 1961, when a full-size representation was displayed beneath an Mi-6 helicopter. In fact, this was a replica of the rocket's final stage complete with nose-fairing which hid all detail of the spacecraft within; and to add further confusion the rocket module had been fitted with a tail annulus supported by eight fins.

Although at the time Western observers thought the tail annulus had been added to stabilize the exhibit beneath the helicopter, the fact that the feature subsequently appeared on official Soviet commemorative stamps and in a documentary film lends support to the view that it was, in fact, a mischievous distortion. At all events, when a Vostok was at last shown without its nose-fairing at the Economic Exhibition in Moscow in April 1965, there was no aerodynamic tail. It was only then that one saw that the re-entry capsule was, in fact, a sphere.

I have questioned leading Soviet space officials on more than one occasion without receiving a satisfactory answer, being advised merely to: 'Believe the Moscow exhibit!' Since the re-entry capsule configuration was kept secret for four years after Gagarin's pioneer flight, one can only conclude that the Russians wanted to keep the West, and particularly America, ignorant of essential design features.

Providing the capsule with an all-enveloping heat shield meant that special provision had to be made for three portholes and the three hatches required for recovery parachutes, ejection seat, and equipment inspection. While the hatches were covered in the same ablative material as the remainder of the capsule, the portholes, made of refractory glass, were deeply recessed in the outer covering.

Within the capsule the cosmonaut was fully protected against emergencies which might otherwise prove fatal. If anything went wrong at lift-off he could escape by blowing the hatch and ejecting in the seat. As the seat rails were inclined in the capsule he would gain height before the parachute opened. Similarly he was able to eject from the capsule after returning from orbit.

The ejection seat, fitted with two ejection rockets, had a detachable back, straps to secure the cosmonaut, and a parachute. In case re-entry occurred in an unscheduled area, possibly over the sea, the seat also contained emergency rations of food and water, radio equipment, and an inflatable dinghy.

Within the cabin the arrangement of instruments and equipment allowed the cosmonaut to perform his flight duties with minimum effort. Instruments were grouped according to their functional role. The console to the left of the cosmonaut had instruments for regulation of temperature and air humidity. There were also radio equipment controls and controls for orientation of the spacecraft during orbital flight.

Vostok's attitude control was assisted by two solar sensors, one automatic and one manual, which allowed the craft to be orientated in a given direction. This, of course, was vital when it came to firing the retro-rockets to reduce orbital speed and initiate re-entry. Vostok was turned about its centre of mass by steering jets fed from compressed gas storage bottles. Switches and buttons on the side panel of the console enabled the cosmonaut to fire the retro-rocket at any point of the orbit.

Immediately facing the cosmonaut was an instrument panel with a clock and counters indicating the number of orbits completed. However, the main instrument was an Earth-globe which revolved synchronously with the spacecraft's movement round the world. This made it possible for the cosmonaut to determine his geographical position at any time and also to predict the area into which his craft would descend should it be necessary to initiate re-entry at any particular point of the orbit. Mounted beneath this panel was a television camera, and below that a porthole incorporating the 'Vzor' optical orientation device. With this instrument the cosmonaut could line up the spacecraft with the Earth's horizon and therefore obtain manual control of the orientation system. The optical system installed in the viewing port comprised two annular mirror-reflectors, a light filter, and a lattice glass. Light rays travelling from the line of the horizon struck the first reflector and, passing through the glass of the porthole, reached the second reflector which directed them through the latticed glass to the cosmonaut's eyes. If the spacecraft's attitude in respect to the vertical axis was correct, he would see the horizon in the form of a circle in his field of vision. Then, using a control handle, the cosmonaut could orientate the craft to bring the line of the horizon into view as a concentric circle. This would be proof of his correct positioning, ensuring that the direction of the Earth's horizon coincided with the course plotted on the glass.

The control handle for manual orientation of the spacecraft was situated on the right-hand side of the cabin together with radio equipment and a food container.

Normally the cosmonaut reclined on his ejection seat with the visor of his helmet open and the suit ventilated with cabin air. In the event of the cabin becoming depressurized, the helmet visor would be closed, pressurization of the suit following automatically. Under such emergency conditions, a reserve supply of compressed oxygen and air would allow time for the cosmonaut to make contact with a ground station, take a decision, select a landing site, and perform an emergency re-entry. The manual control facilities in the cabin allowed the cosmonaut himself to pitch the Vostok at a backward inclined angle prior to firing the retro-rocket. In Vostok it was possible to fire the retro-rockets both automatically (when automatic landing systems were employed) and manually using the controls previously mentioned.

The cabin which had a nitrogen–oxygen atmosphere was designed to maintain normal atmospheric pressure and oxygen content, a carbon dioxide content of not more than 1 per cent, a temperature of 15 to 22°C, and a relative humidity of 30 to 70 per cent. Regeneration of the air, including absorption of CO_2 and water vapour, was assured by means of 'highly active chemical compounds'.

The procedure was automatically controlled. Should the amount of oxygen drop and CO_2 content increase, a sensor gave a signal which adjusted the supply. Similarly, if there was an excess of oxygen, the amount fed into the cabin was automatically adjusted. Humidity was controlled in the same way.

In the event of contamination of the cabin air by harmful admixtures resulting from the function of the human body and the work of the instruments, filters purified the atmosphere. There was also a special temperature control system employing a constant-temperature coolant to conduct heat away from the cabin. The coolant flowed through the temperature control system to a liquid-gas radiator. On the outside of the spacecraft was an automatic radiative heat exchanger, with a system of shutters, which served to maintain the temperature of the cooling agent at the required level.

Food, water, air, and electrical supplies in the Vostok were sufficient for a flight lasting up to 10 days. Had the retro-rocket failed to operate or any other fault occurred preventing the spacecraft's return at the appointed time, the orbit was deliberately chosen to ensure that re-entry would occur within this period as the natural result of atmospheric retardation.

Communications equipment included a Signal radio transmitter operating on a frequency of 19·995 Mc/s for purposes of ground tracking. Two-way radio contact with Earth stations was maintained using short-wave radio on 9·019 and 20·006 Mc/s and ultra-short-wave on 143·625 Mc/s.

The FM channel allowed reliable contact with ground stations up to distances of 930 to 1,240 miles. On short-wave it was possible to maintain communications with ground stations in the Soviet Union over the greater part of the orbit. A tape-recorder was provided in the radio-telephone circuit for recording the cosmonaut's comments for later transmission when Vostok passed over appropriate ground stations.

Vostok's nose-fairing was an interesting feature. It backed on to the attachment ring of the instrument module and final stage and was rocket-ejected after the launch vehicle had penetrated the lower atmosphere. At first sight it appears a dangerous procedure to encase the cosmonaut's re-entry capsule in a massive shroud. What would happen if it failed to separate or something went wrong with the rocket at lift-off?

In fact, the Soviet designers overcame the problem very neatly by sculpting a large cut-out in the side of the fairing through which the cosmonaut could eject after blowing the escape hatch. However, clearly ejection could not be left too late or, despite the protection afforded by his pressure suit, the cosmonaut would perish upon re-entering the Earth's atmosphere.

Many tests of escape systems were made from geophysical rockets and unmanned spacecraft using dogs as test-subjects; there were also high-altitude drops of human subjects from aircraft and balloons.

Much of the work concerned with testing parachutes and ejection seats for the Vostok was performed by the late Colonel Pyotr I. Dolgov. Dolgov was rumoured to have lost his life in a Soviet space mishap. In fact, he died on 3 November 1962, while making a high-altitude parachute jump from the stratospheric balloon Volga. The balloon was at a height of some 25,000 metres (82,021 ft). Major E. Andreev, who jumped first, landed safely; but Dolgov died on the way down.

Voskhod (pages 19 and 27)

Few details of the Voskhod 1 spacecraft were immediately released by the Soviet authorities. There was accommodation for three men, with two seats abreast and one slightly forward. Pressure suits were not worn but kept for emergency use in a locker. Unlike Vostok, the spacecraft did not embody ejection seats.

Although not actually demonstrated, Voskhod was stated to have manœuvre capability and an environmental control system capable of supporting the crew for 1 month. There were two retro-rocket systems for ejecting the capsule from orbit, main and reserve. A retro-rocket landing system (possibly the reserve retro-rocket used in orbit) served to cushion the touchdown as the parachute-supported capsule came within a few feet of the ground, reducing the vertical velocity before impact to perhaps 3 to 4 ft/sec.

Once again the cabin atmosphere was nitrogen–oxygen at sea-level pressure.

An article in *Pravda* on 29 March 1965 described the internal layout of the Voskhod 2 cabin. Two comfortable armchairs, upholstered in white, stand next to each other; close to hand are instrument panels with numerous tumbler switches and luminous dials. Directly overhead are two instrument panels, one of them the control panel for the airlock chamber, equally convenient for either cosmonaut to operate. On the right-hand side, above Belyaev's seat, is the spacecraft's control panel. A long black handle operates the manual orientation system. Just beyond this panel, beneath a transparent safety catch, are the instruments used for re-entry. A red metal hood covers a small black button marked 'Descent TDU' – the Russian initials for retro-engine group. This, of course, is the button that fires the retro-rocket to start re-entry into the atmosphere after the spacecraft has been pitched backwards at the correct angle by the orientation system.

On the other side of the cabin, at upper left, is an instrument panel containing an Earth-globe. As the spacecraft moves round the Earth so the globe revolves indicating the cosmonauts' position at any moment. Adjacent on the same panel are an electric clock, and several needle indicators. Alongside are a signalling board and the optical orientation system control panel.

Ciné and television cameras look down from above. At the extreme left is the airlock hatch. Frosted bulbs are switched on in the airlock chamber and a ciné-camera is installed in a corner. The airlock control panel installed in the cabin is duplicated in the airlock chamber so that, in case of need, the cosmonaut can assume control of the airlock by simply pressing a button. Space-equivalent conditions are then created in the airlock chamber and, at a signal from the cabin, the second hatch swings open to the void of space.

From the photographs of Leonov emerging from Voskhod 2, the airlock was just over 6 ft long by 3 ft diameter. In order to capture movements of the cosmonaut photographically, a number of external directional antennae provided continuous TV transmissions during 2 to 3 r.p.m. roll manœuvres. The improved

TV system – supplying pictures both to the spacecraft cabin and ground stations – employed 625 scan lines and 25 frames per sec. VHF signals were transmitted from the spacecraft on 143·625 Mc/s, ultra-short-wave on 17·365 and 18·035 Mc/s.

In submitting particulars of the Voskhod 1 mission for ratification by the International Aeronautical Federation (FAI), the Soviet authorities gave the aggregate thrust of the multi-stage launch vehicle as 650,000 kg. (1,433,250 lb) using a total of seven engines. This compares with 600,000 kg. (1,323,000 lb) of the Vostok launcher employing six engines. Voskhod 1 and 2 apparently used the same type of launch vehicle with four rocket engines operating at lift-off.

North American X-15 (pages 94-5)

Early experience in the handling and control of aerospace vehicles was obtained with the X-15. Although outwardly the vehicle more closely resembled an aeroplane than a space vehicle, nevertheless it helped to develop techniques for manned spaceflight. Pilots wore full pressure suits, and use was made of gas-jet thrusters for control at high altitudes.

Three aircraft were built for a programme conducted jointly by NASA, the US Air Force, and the US Navy. First glide test from a B-52 parent aircraft was made on 8 June 1959; first powered flight occurred on 17 September 1959.

Power plant is a single Thiokol LR-99 rocket engine with a maximum thrust exceeding 50,000 lb. Propellant is liquid oxygen and anhydrous ammonia.

The attitude control system, developed by Bell Aerosystems, has eight hydrogen peroxide nozzles in the nose and four in the wing-tips. These produce thrusts ranging from 40 to 110 lb and are used to control the X-15 at altitudes where the air is too thin for normal aerodynamic surfaces to act. A three-axis control column at the pilot's left hand applies pitch and yaw control through thrusters in the nose and roll control by thrusters in the wings. This provided invaluable experience upon which to base the design of attitude thrusters for the Mercury spacecraft.

The pressure suit worn by X-15 pilots also represented a

'breakthrough'. Whereas early pressure garments had bulky arm and leg joints, the X-15 suit introduced slip-knit nylon fabric construction which led directly to the lightweight, non-rigid suits subsequently used by the Mercury and Gemini astronauts.

As early as 9 November 1961, an X-15 had achieved a speed of 4,093 m.p.h. (Mach 6·04 at 95,800 ft), following release from the B-52 parent. An altitude of 246,700 ft (over 46 miles) was achieved on 30 April 1962, and since that time performance has been raised considerably. At the time of writing the greatest height achieved is 67 miles.

The scale drawings on pages 94–5 illustrate one of the latest variants of the research vehicle modified for higher speeds and altitudes. It is fitted with two external jettisonable propellant tanks which increase the burning time of the rocket engine from 83 to 150 sec.

This aircraft, the X-15A2, was the first of the three X-15s to achieve powered flight. It was grounded from 9 November 1962 to 25 June 1964, for repairs and modifications following a landing mishap. The added propellant capacity was installed as part of this refurbishment with the aim of increasing the top speed to more than 5,000 m.p.h. The first flight with full external tanks was made successfully on 1 July 1966.

As parts of the X-15A2 could be heated to 1100°C at maximum speed, a thermal protective coating was applied to the structure to keep the temperatures considerably below the original design limit of 650°C. Use was made of a Martin-developed MA-25S sprayable silicone-based ablator which prevents most of the heat from entering the structure through a combination of insulation, re-radiation to the atmosphere, and the formation of 'char'. Refurbishment between flights is accomplished by removing the charred material and spraying on a new coating. When completely coated with ablative material the X-15A2 is some 300 lb heavier.

High-temperature windows were also installed and under consideration for future research was a new wing-tip structure using advanced construction techniques and new lightweight high-temperature materials. The aircraft was being further modified to perform research in hypersonic ramjet propulsion, the 800-lb experimental engine being installed beneath the tail in place of the under-fin. Object of the exercise is to obtain research data for eventual development of air-breathing propulsion systems for flight speeds exceeding 5,000 m.p.h.

McDonnell Mercury (pages 30–5, 40–1)

America's first manned spacecraft was a bell-shaped capsule designed to provide an astronaut with complete experience of spaceflight, including rocket launching, weightlessness (first in sub-orbital and subsequently in orbital flight), re-entry, and land-ing. The configuration was determined primarily by conditions which the capsule would experience under frictional heating when re-entering the Earth's atmosphere.

The astronaut's cabin included a form-fitting couch and an environmental control system providing 100 per cent oxygen at a pressure of 5·5 p.s.i. under space conditions for both cabin and pressure suit. There were two individual control circuits for cabin and suit respectively which normally operated simultaneously for about 28 hr. The astronaut could isolate the suit circuit from the cabin circuit by closing the face-plate of his helmet. The astronaut's pressure suit was not normally inflated except in the case of a failure in the cabin circuit.

The pressure shell of the cabin was double skinned with 0·010 in. titanium, with forward and rear pressure bulkheads also of 0·010 in. titanium. Separated from the inner pressure cone by top-hat stringers was an outer heat-protective skin, made largely of beaded shingles of 0·016 in. René 41 nickel alloy. Between the pressure shell and the outer skin was ceramic-fibre insulation.

The capsule's cylindrical neck section (housing main and reserve landing parachutes) was formed from 0·22 in. beryllium shingles; the adjacent antenna-cone was of Vycor topped by 0·031 in. René 41.

The ablative heat shield of orbital capsules was a glass-fibre reinforced laminated plastic; beryllium was used in the case of sub-orbital capsules where re-entry conditions were less severe. Shields were made detachable so that, following re-entry and release of the main landing parachute, they could be dropped down approximately 4 ft to deploy a perforated impact skirt of rubberized glass-fibre which became a pneumatic cushion on impact with the ocean. After 'softening' the touchdown, it rapidly filled with water to become a sea-anchor maintaining the capsule in an upright floating position.

Two-way communications between the astronaut and ground stations were maintained during flight. Equipment included a voice radio, a receiver for commands from ground stations, and a radio tracking beacon. The astronaut's bio-medical reactions were recorded in flight. Instruments continuously monitored the internal and external environment. Engineering, medical, and scientific data were telemetered to ground receivers.

Four control systems ensured safety of the craft under conditions of flight and re-entry. Eighteen thrusters located in the cylindrical and conical sections of the capsule released bursts of superheated steam for control in pitch, yaw, and roll. Six of these were in a self-contained manual-mechanical system.

Thruster operation depended on passing hydrogen peroxide over a catalyst which decomposed it into steam and oxygen. The peroxide was fed through shut-off valves to the control solenoids under helium pressure and thence to the thrust nozzles.

Mercury's 'autopilot' was the Automatic Stabilization and Control System (ASCA). Its primary function was to detect any unstable motions of the capsule and bring about corrective torques through controlled bursts of thrust; the system could also be programmed to orientate the capsule with the heat shield forward in the path of flight.

A Rate Stabilization and Control System (RSCS) included gyros which sensed rate changes to bring about capsule orientation.

The astronaut was able to assume control by means of the Manual Proportional Control System (MPCS). This had the separate set of six thrusters. The three-axis hand controller worked proportional throttle valves above the thrusters via mechanical linkages; wrist action produced response in yaw, fore and aft movement in pitch, and lateral movement in roll.

Lastly, the Fly-by-Wire System (FBWS) enabled control

column movements to work the throttle valves of the main thrusters electrically. Thus, on 'automatic' and Fly-by-Wire, twelve nozzles were used, those acting in pitch and yaw being mounted in the capsule's cylindrical neck; they delivered a fixed burst of thrust at 1 lb or 24 lb. Roll-control nozzles, located near the base of the capsule at the heat-shield end, gave either 1 lb or 6 lb thrust. The low-thrust nozzles served to bring about minor attitude corrections while the high-thrust nozzles were applied for orientating the capsule and pitching it up in the re-entry attitude. The six manually operated nozzles had variable thrust, the pairs acting in pitch and yaw exerting 4 to 24 lb and the two roll nozzles 1 to 6 lb.

The long curved tubular tank for the hydrogen peroxide thrusters was fitted between the rear pressure bulkhead of the cabin and the heat shield. Stowage for the folded pneumatic landing skirt was in the adjacent compartment.

Attached to the capsule at lift-off was a tower-mounted escape rocket with three canted nozzles. If the main stage engines failed at lift-off or the vehicle deviated from course beyond prescribed limits, errors would be sensed by instruments which would signal the abort system. Immediately, the 50,000-lb thrust escape rocket would separate the capsule from the errant booster for parachute recovery. There was no separate ejection seat for the astronaut. In normal circumstances three 350-lb thrust solid rockets jettisoned the tower when the vehicle had cleared the lower atmosphere.

The retro-rocket pack (secured to the heat shield by metal straps) contained three 1,160-lb thrust solid rockets. With the capsule pitched up at 34°, these were ripple-fired to reduce speed by about 350 m.p.h. Following re-entry a 6-ft diameter conical ribbon-type drogue opened at 21,000 ft. At 10,000 ft this was followed by deployment of the 63-ft diameter ringsail landing parachute stowed in the capsule's cylindrical neck.

McDonnell Gemini (36, 37, 43, 44, 46–59)
The Gemini spacecraft differed in several respects from its predecessor. Although shaped like Mercury it had approximately

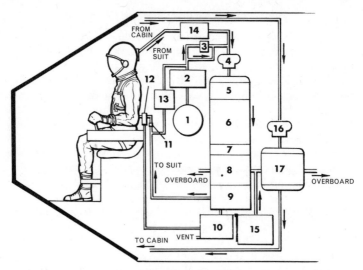

Mercury spacecraft: Environmental Control System (ECS). *Key:* 1. Oxygen; 2. Pressure reducer; 3. Regulator; 4. Fan; 5. Odour absorber; 6. Carbon dioxide absorber; 7. Filter; 8. Heat exchanger; 9. Water separator; 10. Condensate tank; 11. CO_2 sensor; 12. Condensate trap; 13. Emergency flow; 14. Debris trap; 15. Cooling trap; 16. Fan; 17. Heat exchanger.

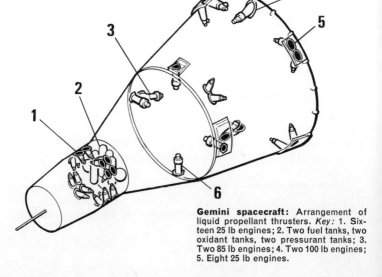

Gemini spacecraft: Arrangement of liquid propellant thrusters. *Key:* 1. Sixteen 25 lb engines; 2. Two fuel tanks, two oxidant tanks, two pressurant tanks; 3. Two 85 lb engines; 4. Two 100 lb engines; 5. Eight 25 lb engines.

Meals consumed aboard Gemini spacecraft were a great improvement over the paste-forms taken on earlier missions. There were two types of food, bite-sized and hydratable. This is the menu for astronauts James Lovell and Edwin Aldrin in Gemini 12; each was allowed 13 meals.

Day 1: Meal A	Calories	Day 3: Meal A	Calories
Applesauce	139	Peaches	98
Sugar-frosted Flakes	139	Strawberry Cereal Cubes	171
Bacon Squares	180	Sausage Patties	223
Cinnamon Toast	56	Cinnamon Toast	56
Cocoa	190	Orange Drink	83
Orange Drink	83	Grapefruit Drink	83
	787		714

Day 1: Meal B		Day 3: Meal B	
Pea Soup	220	Potato Soup	220
Tuna Salad	214	Chicken Salad	237
Cinnamon Toast	56	Beef Sandwiches	138
Date Fruitcake	262	Butterscotch Pudding	311
Pineapple-grapefruit Drink	83	Tea	32
	835		938

Day 1: Meal C		Day 3: Meal C	
Beef Pot Roast	119	Shrimp Cocktail	119
Potato Salad	143	Beef and Gravy	160
Cinnamon Toast	56	Creamed Corn	105
Chocolate Pudding	307	Toasted Bread Cubes	161
Brownies	241	Pineapple Fruitcake	253
Tea	32	Orange-grapefruit Drink	83
	898		881

Day 2: Meal A		Day 4: Meal A	
Applesauce	139	Fruit Cocktail	87
Sugar-frosted Flakes	139	Toasted Oat Cereal	91
Bacon Squares	180	Bacon Squares	180
Cinnamon Toast	56	Ham/Applesauce	127
Cocoa	190	Cinnamon Toast	56
Orange Drink	83	Orange Drink	83
	787	Pineapple-grapefruit Drink	83
			707

Day 2: Meal B		Day 4: Meal B	
Beef/Vegetables	98	Shrimp Cocktail	119
Meat/Spaghetti	70	Chicken/Gravy	92
Cheese Sandwiches	158	Toasted Bread Cubes	161
Apricot Pudding	300	Pineapple Fruitcake	253
Gingerbread	183	Coconut Cubes	206
Grapefruit Drink	83	Orange-grapefruit Drink	83
	892		914

Day 2: Meal C		Day 4: Meal C	
Pea Soup	220	Beef/Vegetables	98
Tuna Salad	214	Meat/Spaghetti	70
Cinnamon Toast	56	Cheese Sandwiches	158
Date Fruitcake	262	Apricot Pudding	300
Pineapple-grapefruit Drink	83	Gingerbread	183
		Grapefruit Drink	83
	835		892

50 per cent greater internal volume. It comprised two principal sections, the re-entry module containing the pressurized crew compartment, and the adapter module.

The crew compartment was a pressurized vessel surrounded by an unpressurized volume in which various systems and fuel were housed. Major components were arranged in modular packages which could be replaced through easily removed external panels without opening the crew compartment or affecting systems already checked out, thereby reducing maintenance and check-out periods prior to lift-off.

Cabin pressurization with 100 per cent oxygen was limited from 5·0 to 5·3 p.s.i. above ambient by the cabin dual pressure regulating valve.

The basic structure reflected the constant effort made in spacecraft design to achieve optimum strength-to-weight ratios. Ring-frame stabilized stringers carried nearly all axial loads, principal metals being titanium and magnesium. The pressure shell itself had a fusion-welded titanium frame attached to side panels and fore and aft bulkheads formed of double thickness, thin-sheet titanium (0·010 in.) with the outer sheet beaded for maximum stiffness.

Following the practice in Mercury the outer surface of the re-entry module was covered by overlapping shingles for aerodynamic and heat protection behind the blunt heat shield. The beaded shingles of 0·016 in. René 41 were thermally isolated from the stringers. Between the pressure compartment and the outer skin was a layer of insulation.

The small end of the re-entry module, skinned with unbeaded beryllium shingles, was capped by a nose-fairing of reinforced plastic and glass-fibre laminate.

The spacecraft's ablative heat shield was based on a load-carrying sandwich of glass fibre. Two five-ply face-plates of resin-impregnated glass cloth were separated by a 0·65-in. thick glass fibre honeycomb core; an additional glass-fibre honeycomb was bonded to the convex side of the sandwich and filled with Dow-Corning DC-325 organic compound. This ablative substance was a paste-like material which hardened in standard atmosphere after being poured into the honeycomb form. Completing the shield on the periphery was a Fiberite ring.

Unlike Mercury, Gemini had no escape tower. Emergency escape – either during the ascent phase to more than 60,000 ft or after re-entry – was provided by ejection seats similar to those in modern military aircraft. There were two large hatches, one for each astronaut, which could be opened and locked open for escape, even under maximum dynamic conditions.

Each hatch had an observation window comprising three glass panes with an air space between each one. The command astronaut's window had two outer glass panes of 96 per cent silica glass and an inner pane of temper-toughened alumino-silicate glass. The co-pilot's window was constructed for optical clarity; instead of the alumino-silicate pane it had a 96 per cent silica glass increased in thickness from 0·22 to 0·38 in. Optical transmission capability of the three panes exceeded 99 per cent for observation and photography.

The astronauts' spacesuits were automatically pressurized with 100 per cent oxygen at 3·7 p.s.i. when the cabin was depressurized for extra-vehicular activity. The 23-lb suit worn by the command pilot had five layers: (1) a white cotton constant wear under-garment with pockets round the waist for bio-medical instrumentation; (2) a blue nylon comfort layer; (3) a black neoprene-coated nylon pressure garment; (4) a restraint layer of nylon link net to restrain the pressure garment and maintain its shape, and (5) a white nylon outer covering.

The EVA suit, weighing 33 lb, had seven layers: (1) the white cotton undergarment with waist instrumentation pockets; (2) the blue nylon comfort layer; (3) the black neoprene-coated nylon pressure garment; (4) a restraint layer of Dacron and Teflon link net; (5) a thermal protective layer of seven layers of aluminized Mylar with spacers between each layer; (6) a micrometeoroid protective layer, and (7) a white nylon outer covering.

Toilet facilities aboard Gemini, as in all early manned space-craft, were not particularly elaborate. Elimination of body waste involved attaching to the body a plastic bag with an adhesive lip. The bag contained germicide to prevent the formation of bacteria and gas. After use the bag was sealed with the adhesive lip and stowed in an empty food container, the contents being brought back for analysis. Urine was delivered into a fitted receptacle connected by hose to either a collection device or an overboard dump.

The spacecraft's adapter module consisted of separate retrograde and equipment sections which were jettisoned prior to re-entry. In the latter was the main power supply comprising two General Electric hydrogen–oxygen fuel-cells; five silver–zinc batteries were located in the equipment bay of the crew compartment for re-entry, landing, and post-landing operations.

Attitude control was obtained from small thrust units (25, 85, and 100 lb) using self-igniting monomethyl hydrazine and nitrogen tetroxide (in contrast to Mercury's hydrogen peroxide). In the retrograde section were six Orbit Attitude and Manœuvring System (OAMS) thrusters. Four of these allowed orbital translation, up, down, left, and right. Two had nozzles facing the re-entry module for rearward translation.

Ten OAMS thrusters in the equipment section gave control in pitch, yaw and roll and provided forward translation in orbit. The re-entry module itself had two rings of eight thrusters for attitude control on the return to Earth.

Infra-red scanners, which sensed spacecraft roll and pitch attitudes with reference to the Earth's horizon, provided attitude information. When switched to automatic control, this system operated almost like an aircraft automatic pilot, leaving the astronauts free to direct their attention elsewhere. Alternatively, manual control in pitch, yaw and roll could be obtained with the three-axis hand controller.

The rendezvous radar, installed in the small end of the spacecraft, had the function of measuring range, range rate, and bearing angle to the target vehicle. This enabled the crew to determine manœuvres necessary for rendezvous and docking. A transponder on the target vehicle received radar impulses and returned them to the spacecraft at a specific frequency and pulse width. Weight of the spacecraft radar was under 70 lb and the power requirement less than 80 W.

Gemini's inertial guidance system comprised a digital computer, the inertial platform electronics package, and a power supply. The computer was a general-purpose, binary, digital type capable of performing high-speed integrations, input-output conversions, arithmetic computations, and rendezvous timing functions. It had a non-destructive memory and automatically indicated any fault. A manual data insertion unit allowed the astronauts to place up to 100 messages into the computer, and served as a back-up for the digital command system. Three push buttons on a control panel allowed the astronauts to enter, cancel, or read out the displayed data.

The inertial measuring unit, operating in conjunction with the computer, measured all accelerations applied to the spacecraft. It depended on a stabilized platform containing three miniature integrating gyros and three pendulous accelerometers. The system served both as an attitude reference and a navigation reference during rendezvous, re-entry, and landing.

Heat-protective paints and coatings were responsible for the dark appearance of the re-entry module. The white finish on the adapter module, on the other hand, allowed maximum release of heat brought to the metal surface by coolant channels beneath the skin. This part of the spacecraft was made of circular aluminium-alloy frames, extruded magnesium-alloy stringers, and magnesium skin. The T-shaped stringers had a hollow bulbous section allowing the passage of liquid coolant, which transferred heat generated in the vehicle to the skin for radiation into space.

A cloth cover over the open end of the adapter module protected the internal equipment from solar radiation after separation from the launch vehicle. This was made of Vitron-impregnated glass cloth with vapour-deposited gold.

Recovery of the spacecraft from orbit was effected by firing four solid-propellant retro-rockets, each producing 2,500 lb thrust by 5·5 sec. and operating in series with overlap. Following re-entry, at about 60,000 ft, an 18-ft diameter ringsail parachute was deployed by a mortar; then, at 10,000 ft, an 84-ft diameter ringsail parachute inflated to provide stable descent towards the sea at a vertical velocity of 30 ft/sec.

MANNED SPACEFLIGHT CHRONOLOGY:
THE FIRST FIVE YEARS

Astronaut	Spacecraft (Name or Call-sign)	Country	Launch Date	Flight Duration
Gagarin	Vostok 1 (Swallow)	USSR	12.4.61	1 hr. 48 min.
Shepard	Mercury MR-3 (Freedom 7)	USA	5.5.61	15 min. 22 sec.
Grissom	Mercury MR-4 (Liberty Bell 7)	USA	21.7.61	15 min. 37 sec.
Titov	Vostok 2 (Eagle)	USSR	6.8.61	25 hr. 18 min.
Glenn	Mercury MA-6 (Friendship 7)	USA	20.2.62	4 hr. 55 min.
Carpenter	Mercury MA-7 (Aurora 7)	USA	24.5.62	4 hr. 56 min.
Nikolayev	Vostok 3 (Falcon)	USSR	11.8.62	94 hr. 22 min.
Popovich	Vostok 4 (Golden Eagle)	USSR	12.8.62	70 hr. 57 min.
Schirra	Mercury MA-8 (Sigma 7)	USA	3.10.62	9 hr. 13 min.
Cooper	Mercury MA-9 (Faith 7)	USA	15.5.63	34 hr. 20 min.
Bykovsky	Vostok 5 (Hawk)	USSR	14.6.63	119 hr. 6 min.
Tereshkova	Vostok 6 (Sea Gull)	USSR	16.6.63	70 hr. 50 min.
Feoktistov Komarov Yegorov	Voskhod 1 (Ruby)	USSR	12.10.64	24 hr. 17 min.
Belyaev Leonov	Voskhod 2 (Diamond)	USSR	18.3.65	26 hr. 2 min.
Grissom Young	Gemini GT-3	USA	23.3.65	4 hr. 53 min.
McDivitt White	Gemini GT-4	USA	3.6.65	97 hr. 56 min.

Astronaut	Spacecraft (Name or Call-sign)	Country	Launch Date	Flight Duration
Cooper Conrad	Gemini GT-5	USA	21.8.65	190 hr. 56 min.
Borman Lovell	Gemini GT-7	USA	4.12.65	330 hr. 35 min.
Schirra Stafford	Gemini GT-6	USA	15.12.65	25 hr. 51 min.
Armstrong Scott	Gemini GT-8	USA	16.3.66	10 hr. 42 min.
Stafford Cernan	Gemini GT-9	USA	3.6.66	72 hr. 21 min.
Young Collins	Gemini GT-10	USA	18.7.66	70 hr. 46 min.
Conrad Gordon	Gemini GT-11	USA	12.9.66	71 hr. 17 min.
Lovell Aldrin	Gemini GT-12	USA	11.11.66	94 hr. 34 min.

Spacecraft times certified to the FAI by the Soviet authorities for homologation of flights as world records were: Vostok 3, 94 hr. 9 min. 59 sec.; Vostok 4, 70 hr. 43 min. 48 sec.; Vostok 5, 118 hr. 56 min. 41 sec.; Vostok 6, 70 hr. 40 min. 48 sec.

The Lunar Project

The evolution of the spacecraft can be traced to many independent sources in many countries. Its theoretical basis was laid at the turn of the last century by Konstantin E. Tsiolkovsky, the father of Soviet cosmonautics, and Professor Hermann Oberth in Germany contributed hugely to the theory and practice of space travel in his classic work, *Die Rakete zu den Planetenraumen*, first published in 1923. Many other workers were active in this period; but the practical development of large liquid-propellant rockets, under Major-General Walter Dornberger and Dr Wernher von Braun at Peenemünde between 1938 and 1945, turned the dream into potential reality.

The BIS Spaceship (page 92)

Credit for the first engineering analysis is due to the pre-war Technical Committee of the British Interplanetary Society. In 1938 the Society set out to examine the practical requirements for a vehicle capable of carrying three men to the Moon and back. The results of a design-study were published in 1939.* Although there were obvious shortcomings, particularly in terms of propulsion and post-lunar re-entry into the Earth's atmosphere, the study was remarkably perceptive of modern spacecraft techniques.

The cylindrical launch vehicle, 100 ft tall by 20 ft diameter, weighed 1,000 tonnes. Its propulsion system comprised 2,490 solid-propellant motors arranged as a honeycomb in steps or banks. The pressurized cabin was situated in the nose and clusters of rockets were built up layer by layer beneath it, so that the spent motors in the first stage dropped off and the next layer fired, and so on, until the vehicle reached escape velocity. Ignition was governed by an automatic trajectory programming device and liquid-propellant vernier motors were to give fine control of velocity and manœuvre. It was proposed to conduct launching from a flooded caisson sunk in a high-level lake near the Equator.

More layers of rockets were assumed to be used in braking against the Moon's gravitational pull and for the return flight. A unique feature of the design was that the vehicle employed extendable landing legs permitting a vertical touchdown after rocket braking. Therefore the spacecraft was placed in the correct attitude for re-launching from the leg supports. Small rocket motors were incorporated for mid-course correction of the ship's path, and for manœuvring prior to touchdown on the Moon.

From these few details it can be seen that as early as 1939 big advances had been made from the theoretical and visual conceptions of the 1920s. The BIS study envisaged the use of inertial navigation instruments. Such devices have since reached a high state of perfection for submarines, missiles, and aircraft. Another novelty – a 'coelostat' – was made and demonstrated. This, the

* See *Journal of the British Interplanetary Society*, January and July, 1939.

first instrument intended specifically for a spacecraft, was an optical device designed to provide a stationary view of the heavens from a vehicle which was being rotated to provide the crew with a sensation of weight induced by centrifugal force.

Attention was paid to the physiological needs and safety of the crew, including the use of contour couches. A double-walled pressure cabin was proposed for good thermal insulation and to minimize risk of puncture by meteorites. Although the problem of re-entry into the Earth's atmosphere following the return from the Moon received little attention, a jettisoned heat-resisting nose-cone was shown protecting the vehicle from frictional heating during the ascent from Earth. Many of these ideas have since been applied in missiles and spacecraft.

The drawing on page 92 is a reconstruction in colour of an original drawing by the late R. A. Smith dated 1947. It represents a re-evaluation of the pre-war BIS Lunar Spaceship in terms of liquid-propellant technology. The vehicle was designed to lift off from the Moon using the leg-supported base section as a launch platform. A quarter of a century later this was to become the technique for re-launching an actual manned spacecraft from the lunar surface in project Apollo.

Apollo Command Module (pages 65, 66, 68, 75, 86, 87–91)

This module houses the three-man Apollo crew and is the only part of the vehicle that returns from the lunar mission. It has the shape of a cone approximately 12 ft high and 12·8 ft across the base. The habitable volume is 218 ft^3. Fully loaded at lift-off it weighs approximately 11,000 lb.

The double-walled structure consists of an inner pressure shell and an outer heat shield separated by structural stringers. A micro-quartz fibre between the walls provides thermal insulation. The outer structure is a three-piece heat shield (covering top, sides, and blunt end of the capsule), constructed of brazed honeycomb stainless steel to which is bonded an epoxy resin ablative coating. Thickness of the ablative material varies according to the expected aerodynamic heat distribution over the vehicle.

The inner pressure shell, made of aluminium honeycomb bonded between sheets of aluminium, is the primary load-carrying structure. An access tunnel, capped by a pressure cover, extends from the crew compartment to the apex. The space round the tunnel just below the apex is divided into four sections by stiffeners; these house recovery parachutes, pyrotechnics, and electronic equipment.

The cabin is pressurized with 100 per cent oxygen at 5 p.s.i. ambient by the Environmental Control System (ECS). Other systems include S-band communications, guidance and navigation, and attitude control.

The Reaction Control System (RCS) provides control in pitch, yaw, and roll after separation from the service module for re-entry into the Earth's atmosphere. Twelve units mounted near the base of the module deliver 93 lb of thrust through ablative chambers. There are two sets of thrusters for each control axis. Fuel is monomethyl hydrazine and oxidant nitrogen tetroxide. Thrust can be applied automatically from the ASCS or independently by astronaut manual control. At launch an escape tower is fitted for separation of the command module under the action of the Emergency Detection System (EDS). The escape rocket would be operated during powered flight if there was catastrophic loss of thrust in the main-stage engines, or if excessive angular rates of pitch, yaw, or roll developed. These actions, automatically sensed by the EDS, would either fire the escape system directly or provide data for the crew to exercise manual control of abort procedures.

The wing-like canard surfaces (see drawing) are opened by explosives 11 sec. after the escape rocket fires. They serve to stabilize the command module blunt end forward prior to deployment of the drogue parachutes. There is also a pitch motor to deflect the craft into a recovery trajectory.

The 'Q-ball' at the top of the escape tower contains pressure sensors for determining flight angles of attack and dynamic pressure after lift-off.

It is also possible to use the engine of the service module as an escape system, independently of the tower-mounted rocket. In this case the command and service modules would separate following the abort manœuvre.

The landing system caters for pad abort, high altitude abort (up to 70,000 ft), and normal re-entry after flight. Following descent to 25,000 ft above sea-level, a barometric pressure switch fires an explosive charge to jettison the apex heat shield over the parachute compartment. Two seconds later, two 13-ft diameter nylon conical ribbon drogue parachutes are mortar-deployed for stabilization and deceleration of the command module. Drogues are reefed for 8 sec., then fully opened. At approximately 10,000 ft three pilot parachutes are deployed, also by mortar. Each pulls one of the main 83·5-ft ringsail parachutes from its container. Main parachutes open in reefed condition, providing deceleration without excessive opening shock. After 8 sec. reefing lines are cut automatically and main parachutes fully inflate for final landing at approximately 27·5 ft/sec. Each main parachute weighs 127 lb including canopy, riser, and deployment bag. Total weight of the landing system is approximately 540 lb.

In a Third Report on the work of the Board investigating the fire in Apollo spacecraft AS 204 (pages 179–81), certain recommendations were made mainly affecting modifications to the Apollo command module. These were:

That combustible materials now used be replaced wherever possible with non-flammable materials, that non-metallic materials that *are* used be arranged to maintain fire breaks, that systems for oxygen or liquid combustibles be made fire-resistant, and that full flammability tests be conducted with a mockup of the new configuration.

That a more rapidly and more easily operated hatch be designed and installed.

That on-the-pad emergency procedures be revised to recognise the possibility of cabin fire.

In addition the Board drew attention to

> a number of components, sub-systems, techniques and practices which it felt could be improved to increase crew safety and mission reliability. These included findings in the environmental control system, solder joints, location of wiring, electrical equipment qualification and design, and the development of checkout procedures.

The Board did not recommend a change in the use of pure oxygen in the spacesuit for either pre-launch or orbital operations, nor did it recommend that cabin atmosphere for operations in space should be changed from 5 p.s.i. pure oxygen. However, it did recommend 'that the trade-offs between one and two-gas atmospheres be re-evaluated' and that pressurized oxygen no longer be used in pre-launch operations.

Apollo Service Module (pages 65, 66, 79–85, 87–9)

This 12·9-ft long cylindrical vehicle supports the command module; the fully fuelled weight is approximately 55,000 lb. The structure is formed of 1-in. thick panels of aluminium honeycomb sandwich construction supported by six radial beams. Tension ties attaching the service module to the command module are released explosively to separate the modules prior to re-entry.

At the base of the module is the spacecraft's main propulsion unit used for mid-course correction, braking the vehicle into lunar orbit, and for the return flight. The engine, which is gimballed by two electrically operated servo actuators, delivers a maximum thrust of 21,900 lb. Propellant is self-igniting unsymmetrical dimethyl hydrazine and oxidant nitrogen tetroxide fed by helium pressure. There are four main propellant tanks.

The same propellant combination (in separate tanks) is used to power four independent and identical sets of four 100-lb thrusters of the RCS. All sixteen thrusters are mounted outside the service module, being fed from internal tanks under helium pressure.

The sets of four thrusters providing control in pitch, yaw, and roll are mounted with 90° spacing round the service module, and thrusters are mounted in a 90° relationship to each other. Thrust can be applied: (1) to force main engine propellant into the lower end of the tank for engine restarting; (2) for making minor orbital and mid-course manœuvres, and (3) for docking with the lunar module.

Apollo Adapter Module (page 65)

This 28-ft long, 3,900-lb, tapered section serves as the interstage fairing between the third stage of the Saturn 5 launch vehicle and the Apollo spacecraft. It also garages the lunar module. The eight panels hinge back like petals to allow the lunar module to be pulled free after Apollo has been injected into the translunar orbit. The panels are of aluminium honeycomb sandwich construction 1·75 in. thick; four have linear explosive charges installed at the panel junctions.

Apollo Lunar Module (pages 65, 67, 71–5, 80–5)

The spacecraft, designed to land two astronauts on the Moon after release from the Apollo parent craft in lunar orbit, has two main components; a *descent stage* incorporating the landing gear and an *ascent stage* containing the pressurized crew cabin. Earth launch weight is approximately 32,500 lb.

Constructed largely of aluminium alloy, the structural shell of the ascent stage has an external composite layer of insulation and a thin aluminium skin affording the astronauts thermal and micrometeoroid protection. The outer skin and the inner pressure shell are approximately 3 in. apart. The cabin, a 92-in. diameter cylinder, is stiffened by 2-in. deep circumferential frames spaced approximately 10 in. apart and located between the structural skin and the thermal shield. The compartment has two triangular cabin windows in the front-face bulkhead, an overhead docking window on the left side, a forward hatch, controls and displays, and astronaut support equipment.

Directly behind the cabin is a smaller compartment containing

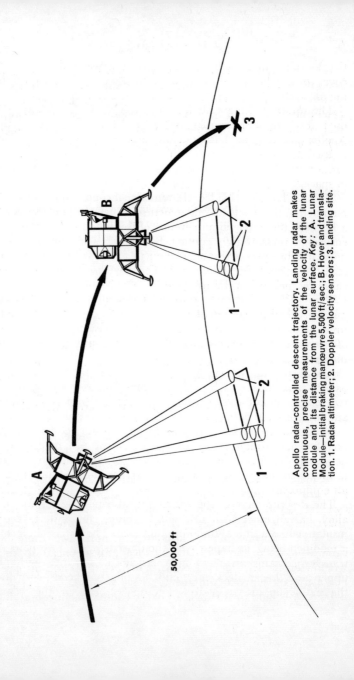

Apollo radar-controlled descent trajectory. Landing radar makes continuous, precise measurements of the velocity of the lunar module and its distance from the lunar surface. *Key:* A. Lunar Module—initial braking manœuvre 5,500 ft/sec.; B. Hover and translation. 1. Radar altimeter; 2. Doppler velocity sensors; 3. Landing site.

50,000 ft

the docking hatch, ECS, and equipment stowage. A removable cover provides access to the 3,500-lb thrust ascent engine plumbing and valves.

The upper docking tunnel at the top of the ascent stage is used for astronaut transfer to the command module of the Apollo parent. The hatch below the centre control consoles is used for leaving and entering the spacecraft on the lunar surface and for extra-vehicular transfer of crew and equipment in space.

Hatches have pre-loaded elastomeric silicone compound seals mounted in the lunar module structure. When the latch is closed, a lip near the outer circumference of the hatch enters the seal, ensuring a pressure-tight contact. Both hatches open inwards and normal cabin pressurization is used to force the hatch into the seal. To open either hatch, it is necessary to depressurize the cabin by means of a dump valve.

The ECS maintains pressure, temperature, and relative humidity for a maximum of 48 hr. The cabin can be refilled four times with 100 per cent oxygen, and the astronauts' portable life-support system, five times. With a cabin pressure of 5 p.s.i. maximum leakage rate is 0·2 lb/hr.

Aft of the midsection pressure bulkhead are two gaseous oxygen tanks for the ECS (which supplies the cabin atmosphere), two helium tanks for ascent-stage main-propellant pressurization, and inverters and batteries for electrical power supply. Propellant tanks are located on both sides in the non-pressurized area. They hold fuel and oxidant for the ascent engine and fuel, oxidant and helium for the RCS. Two ECS water tanks are located overhead in the ascent stage, with two gaseous oxygen storage tanks in the aft equipment bay.

The descent stage of the spacecraft, also built in aluminium alloy, has an inner structure with an outer composite layer of insulation and a thin aluminium-alloy skin. The outer skin forms a modified octagon shape round the descent stage. Two pairs of transverse beams arranged in a cruciform, together with an upper and lower deck and end closure bulkheads, provide the main support structure. The space between the beam

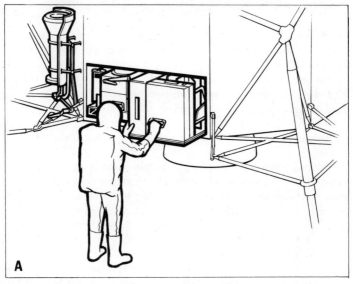

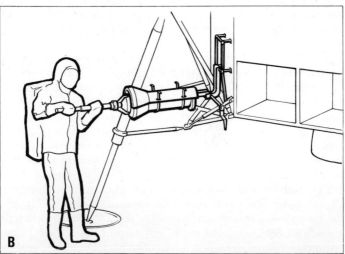

Deployment sequence of the **Apollo Lunar Surface Experiment Package (ALSEP)** described on pages 190–2. The SNAP-27 radioisotope generator is developed by the General Electric Company of the USA under the direction of the US Atomic Energy Commission. A. Apollo astronaut removes ALSEP components from stowage in base of lunar module. B. Radioisotope fuel capsule is removed from storage cask by hinging cask into a horizontal position

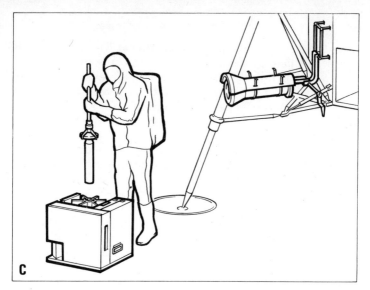

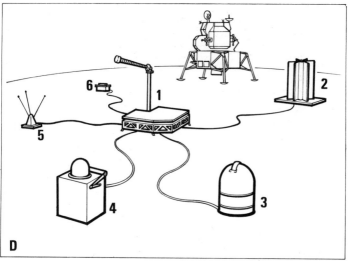

and engaging fuel capsule with handling tool. C. Fuel capsule is inserted into the SNAP-27 generator and locked into position. Full power operation occurs some 90 min. later. D. ALSEP components deployed to operate unattended in light and darkness for about one year. *Key:* 1. Aerial, data management and power distribution box; 2. SNAP-27 generator; 3. Seismometer; 4. Solar wind meter; 5. Magnetometer; 6. Ion detector.

inter-sections forms the centre compartment which contains the throttleable descent engine. Maximum thrust is 10,500 lb.

Surrounding the engine are four propellant tanks, two oxidant tanks being located between the vertical beams and two fuel tanks between the horizontal beams. In the diagonal bays, adjacent to the propellant tanks, are helium, oxygen, and water tanks, batteries, lunar surface antenna, and scientific equipment.

The cantilever landing gear is mounted on outriggers that extend from the end of each of the two pairs of transverse beams. Each of the four legs consists of a primary strut and footpad, a 'drive-out' mechanism, two secondary struts, two down-lock mechanisms, and a truss. All struts have crushable attenuator inserts as a means of absorbing impact loads at touchdown.

The landing legs remain folded until the spacecraft arrives in lunar orbit. The landing gear uplocks are then explosively released and springs in each drive-out mechanism extend the landing gear. Once extended each leg is locked in place by the two down-lock mechanisms.

At the time of lunar lift-off (or 'abort' before lunar landing) the two stages are separated by firing four explosive bolts at the stage interconnection. At the same time interstage wiring is explosively severed and other connexions mechanically released.

Apollo Applications Programme

The enormous potential of the Saturn launch vehicles, Apollo spacecraft, launch facilities, and support equipment developed for the lunar mission, of course, extends far beyond the initial objective of placing men on the Moon for 24–36 hr. The Apollo Applications Programme represents an effort to apply the basic technology to missions of far wider significance, both in the long-term exploration of space and in programmes which have direct economic value to man on Earth.

A prime target is to keep men in orbit from one month to a year when opportunities for important scientific and technological experiments should increase substantially. NASA officials have emphasized that extended flight experience is also necessary to provide experience on which to base sound decisions affecting the future development of spaceflight, such as permanent manned facilities in orbit or manned flights to the planets. Initially, effort is being directed towards extending the flight capability of existing Apollo hardware to include manned astronomical and Earth observations from space and the continued exploration of the Moon.

What is envisaged in terms of the orbital programme is an embryonic space station. However, this does not entail the assembly of a single rigid structure but rather a modular grouping of different functional components, made to orbit together some 320 miles above the Earth.

The idea has obvious attractions since orbital facilities can be expanded and contracted at will by the simple expedient of adding and subtracting different modules. It is also a technique that lends itself to future international development. For example, separate laboratory modules developed in the Soviet Union and the United States could orbit in formation benefiting from mutual support and rescue facilities. The initial work in America, however, is restricted to the development of existing hardware as a purely experimental exercise, using launchers, spacecraft, and equipment developed in the Apollo programme.

Central to the scheme is an 'orbital workshop' formed from the orbiting S-IVB stage of an Uprated Saturn 1. The object is to place the specially modified S-IVB into the desired circular orbit, with the view of having astronauts sent up in another spacecraft to convert its empty hydrogen tank into a rudimentary space-station. Mounted on a framework at the top end of the tank is a 65-in. diameter airlock and docking adapter, built by McDonnell. The latter has a multiple docking adapter which provides five docking points for visiting spacecraft. The equipment includes both a power supply and an environmental control system. The latter is capable of pressurizing the S-IVB's 21ft 8-in. diameter tank with a nitrogen–oxygen atmosphere at about 5 p.s.i. (with between 1·5 and 2 p.s.i. of nitrogen). The tank has a total volume of 10,000 ft^3.

The project, outlined in 1967 by Dr George E. Mueller, NASA's Associate Administrator for Manned Space Flight,

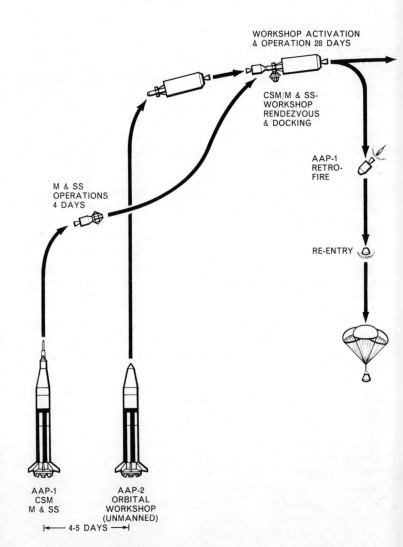

WORKSHOP ACTIVATION
& OPERATION 28 DAYS

CSM/M & SS-
WORKSHOP
RENDEZVOUS
& DOCKING

AAP-1
RETRO-
FIRE

M & SS
OPERATIONS
4 DAYS

RE-ENTRY

AAP-1
CSM
M & SS

AAP-2
ORBITAL
WORKSHOP
(UNMANNED)

|← 4-5 DAYS →|

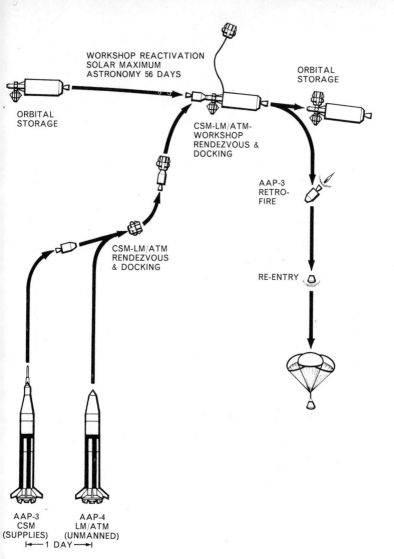

WORKSHOP REACTIVATION
SOLAR MAXIMUM
ASTRONOMY 56 DAYS

ORBITAL
STORAGE

ORBITAL
STORAGE

CSM-LM/ATM-
WORKSHOP
RENDEZVOUS &
DOCKING

AAP-3
RETRO-
FIRE

CSM-LM/ATM
RENDEZVOUS
& DOCKING

RE-ENTRY

AAP-3
CSM
(SUPPLIES)

AAP-4
LM/ATM
(UNMANNED)

⊢—1 DAY—⊣

Apollo Applications payloads orbited separately by four Uprated Saturn 1 launch vehicles are clustered to form a rudimentary space station. Components are defined on page 230.

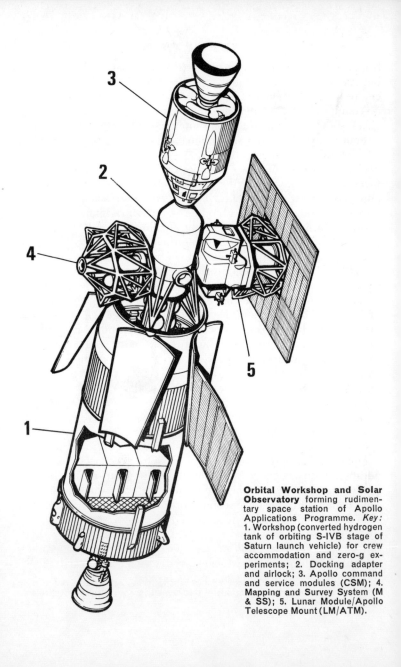

Orbital Workshop and Solar Observatory forming rudimentary space station of Apollo Applications Programme. *Key:* 1. Workshop (converted hydrogen tank of orbiting S-IVB stage of Saturn launch vehicle) for crew accommodation and zero-g experiments; 2. Docking adapter and airlock; 3. Apollo command and service modules (CSM); 4. Mapping and Survey System (M & SS); 5. Lunar Module/Apollo Telescope Mount (LM/ATM).

begins with the orbiting of a manned AAP-1 spacecraft comprising Apollo service and command modules. The craft carries an
engineering test model of Mapping and Survey System (M and
SS) equipment for use in future lunar-orbit missions. This will be
checked out by the astronauts as an independent experiment.

Four to five days later will follow the launching into a similar
orbit of the S-IVB stage – the AAP-2 – complete with airlock and
docking adapter. The two spacecraft will rendezvous and stay
together for 28 days while the Apollo crew activate the workshop
and perform set experiments. The M and SS package, carried
into orbit within the adapter module of the Saturn launch vehicle,
is stored on one of the side docking attachments and the spacecraft itself at the forward docking position (see drawing opposite).

Conversion of the S-IVB stage into habitable quarters proceeds
as follows: First the visiting astronauts release pressure inside the
hydrogen tank and disconnect electrical wiring. Next, they
remove a 43-in. diameter circular hatch in the top end of the
tank, bolting in its place the ring support of flexible bellows which
extend from the adjacent airlock. The tank can now be pressurized with the nitrogen–oxygen atmosphere, after which the men
can pass directly through the airlock into the tank interior, taking
with them prefabricated parts and equipment stowed in the
airlock and docking assembly.

First they unroll circular fabric diaphragms designed to fit the
tank diameter and fix these to form floors and ceilings using
anchorages previously built into the tank structure. The fabric
is stretched tight with ropes. This will divide the tank into separate
compartments approximately 10 ft high, with access between and
additional 'attic' space above and below. Racks and other
prefabricated items can then be brought in and attached to the
tank baffles, until the lower compartment is completely fitted out
with different areas for sleeping, food preparation, waste management, physical exercise and recreation, divided by canvas walls.
On the second floor will be work areas for engineering and
scientific experiments. Dr Mueller has described the procedure as
somewhat akin to building a ship in a bottle.

Experiments are many and varied. They include jet-shoes

proposed by the Langley Research Laboratory for a different approach to manœuvrability in space. These are basically 'roller skates' with gas-jet nozzles on the ends so that an astronaut can use them to manœuvre in the weightless environment.

Astronauts will also learn how to service heat exchangers under weightlessness, and how to work high-pressure gas systems. The Gemini programme showed there is still much to learn about the operation of conventional apparatus under space conditions. A heat-pipe experiment, developed at Los Alamos, involves a device which makes use of convection currents of gas to transfer large amounts of heat from one end of a pipe to another and capillary forces to carry it back.

Another experiment concerns what happens to the flammability of materials when there is a combination of oxygen, nitrogen, and zero-g, i.e. in the absence of ordinary convection currents.

The full list of experiments originally specified for this programme is as follows:

Engineering
(a) suits and lunar hardware;
(b) ST-124 removal and disassembly;
(c) zero-g flammability;
(d) astronaut EVA equipment;
(e) habitability/crew quarters;
(f) high-pressure gas expulsion;
(g) heat exchanger service;
(h) surface absorbed materials;
(i) tube joining in space;
(j) electron beam welding;

Medical
(k) vectorcardiogram;
(l) metabolic activity;
(m) cardiovascular function assessment;
(n) bone and muscle changes;
(o) human vestibular function;
(p) neurological study (EEG);
(q) time and motion study;

Department of Defence
(*r*) integrated maintenance;
(*s*) suit donning and sleep station evaluation;
(*t*) alternate restraints evaluation;
(*u*) expandable airlock technology;

Technology
(*v*) meteoroid impact and erosion;
(*w*) jet-shoes;
(*x*) meteoroid velocity;
(*y*) heat pipe.

After the initial 28-day work period has expired, the astronauts will shut down systems in the workshop and return to Earth in the AAP-1 command module.

Within three to six months, the next phase of operations will begin with the launching into orbit of another manned spacecraft comprising AAP-3 command and service modules. A day later a second launching will place into a similar orbit an Apollo Telescope Mount (ATM), in an experiment designed to evaluate the use of a man-monitored astronomical observatory. The ATM platform, called AAP-4, is mounted on a structural rack attached to the modified ascent stage of an Apollo lunar module.

After the manned Apollo has rendezvoused and docked with the ATM, the pair will rendezvous and dock with the orbiting workshop. When required for observation, the ATM can be undocked for independent operation.

This second mission could last a maximum of 56 days. It involves observation of the Sun near the period of maximum solar activity in 1969–70, and is expected to provide valuable experience necessary to the design and operation of future large telescopes in space which may have to be man-monitored or at least man-maintained.

The rack which supports the 150-in. long by 80-in. diameter telescope tube has control gyros for coarse pointing, and the tube itself is gimbal-mounted in the frame. The gimbals allow the tube about 5° freedom of movement for fine-pointing control. Supported by a framework at the top end of the telescope is an array of solar cells providing power supply. The astronaut-astronomer gains access to the telescope tube (i.e. for retrieval of exposed film) directly from the Apollo ascent stage.

Astronomical instruments carried in the telescope tube for solar observation allow study of solar flares, the white-light corona, ultra-violet and x-rays, and the solar corona. Many of the results will take the form of spectrographs (in which light is split into its component parts) rather than direct image photography.

At the end of the mission, the workshop will again be shut down leaving the ATM *in situ* for further use. The next phases of operation may involve the incorporation of new equipment and more complete evaluation of the astronomical potential of the man-monitored system.

Development of the AAP-1 and AAP-3 ferry vehicles necessitated modifications to the basic Apollo command and service modules. A nitrogen–oxygen atmosphere life-support system was specified for the long-duration missions with increased capacity fuel-cells and extra cryogenic fuel storage. Modifications to the command module were to allow four to six men to be carried on short-duration supply missions, and there was provision for making recovery on land instead of at sea.

The object of land recovery was to enable command modules to be refurbished without problems of salt-water contamination, and also to reduce the number of naval forces tied up in recovery operations.

The favoured method of capsule recovery involved a gliding parachute of high lift-drag ratio allowing both a degree of directional control and reduced vertical velocity. The capsule-parachute combination is manœuvred on the way down and visual, manual, and automatic controls are provided in the cabin.

A scheme was also being developed which allowed impact with the ground to be 'softened' by the use of retro-rockets, similar to the system used in the Soviet Voskhod capsule. The braking rockets are designed to ignite within 5 to 10 ft of the ground, reducing the impact from a possible 10 to 20 ft/sec. to 3 to 4 ft/sec.

In preparing for manned space activity of the kind involved in the orbiting workshop and ATM, intensive studies were made at various NASA research centres over a period of some five years. During this period – between 1963 and 1966 – under NASA contract, the Douglas Missile and Space Systems Division produced their famous study for a Manned Orbiting Research Laboratory (MORL). This had the object of defining a multi-purpose space station, capable of supporting programmes for scientific research, development of technology in support of extended manned missions, and applications promoting human welfare. Earth-related observations include assistance to agri-culture, forestry, geology, hydrology, geography, meteorology, and oceanography.

Some time ago, and particularly in the light of results obtained in the Gemini programme, it became apparent that the large-scale 'overview' of our planet made possible by space techniques could assist in the conservation of the Earth's food, water, and mineral resources. For example, underwater geological for-mations showed up clearly in some of the photographs taken by the Gemini astronauts and it was possible to see the effects of ocean currents on the colour of the water. Faults in the Earth's crust, hitherto unsuspected, also stood out clearly.

There was evidence of salinity in the soil in cotton-growing areas in Texas, and further development of space-sensing tech-niques may allow world-wide survey of agricultural soil con-ditions. By changing the spectral value of the photographic image obtained from orbit, it may also be possible to pin-point certain crop diseases, a technique already possible from aircraft. A typical picture shows healthy fields of potatoes in red; those suffering from blight in black.

The former President of the American Institute of Aeronautics and Astronautics, Dr Raymond L. Bishlinghoff, writing on 'Space and the World's Needs' (*Astronautics and Aeronautics*, November 1966), drew particular attention to the potential of oceanic survey.

> Satellites have been suggested for observing surface thermal conditions and sea-surface roughness, shoal and coastal

mapping, ice surveillance, and marine life observations. The productivity of fisheries in the United States has increased less than 10 per cent in the last decade. This important source of foodstuffs will obviously not keep pace with population increases unless more can be done to improve off-shore production. . . . Any aid provided by spacecraft sensors in recording the movement of plankton and other variables that affect the migration of fishing grounds could materially influence the productivity of the fishing industry.

A typical Earth-resources test-payload being developed in the Apollo Applications Programme includes the following instruments: (*a*) multiband camera; (*b*) metric camera; (*c*) panoramic camera; (*d*) tracking telescope; (*e*) wide-angle imager; (*f*) radar imager; (*g*) radar altimeter and scatterometer; (*h*) laser altimeter; (*i*) infra-red spectrometer and radiometer; (*j*) passive microwave imager and radiometer; (*k*) absorption spectroscope, and (*l*) ultra-violet spectrometer.

Many of these instrumentation techniques stem from work undertaken by NASA with space probes for reconnoitring the Moon, Venus, and Mars; and not a little is owed to reconnaissance and surveillance techniques developed by the US Air Force in the Midas (Missile Defence Alarm System) and Samos (Satellite and Missile Observation System) programmes.

The Manned Orbiting Research Laboratory (MORL), which embraced all these possibilities for remote sensing of natural resources, is illustrated on page 93. A six- to nine-man vehicle weighing under 34,000 lb, it offered in addition to station-keeping capability, an experimental capacity of 1,650 ft^3 of volume and 2 kW of power.

Launched unmanned into a low-inclination orbit near the Earth by an Uprated Saturn 1, it would be initially manned, and subsequently resupplied, by Apollo command and service modules launched by the same type of Saturn vehicle. But, of course, MORL was never intended to be built; merely to guide future development.

Apollo Applications experiments will develop techniques for

man's participation in such fields as orbital meteorology, communications, and remote sensing of Earth resources. Low-altitude orbits at medium and high inclinations have been studied for meteorology and natural resources missions around 1970. It is also planned to test manned Apollo operations in synchronous orbit 22,300 miles above the Equator. This may serve to develop operational techniques for communicating between a spacecraft in synchronous orbit, another in a low orbit, and ground control stations. It may also lead to the servicing of large direct-broadcasting satellites beaming television programmes directly to domestic or community-centre receivers on Earth.

Extended lunar missions planned for Apollo include both orbital mapping of the Moon's surface using the M and SS and direct surface exploration. This will affect decisions concerning the establishment of semi-permanent or extensive research facilities on the Moon.

Lunar surface missions in the early 1970s are planned to provide up to 2 weeks stay-time at selected lunar sites for extensive selenological and biological exploration. Small roving vehicles will allow travel up to 15 miles from the landed spacecraft. Drills will be used for sub-surface sampling and vertical profile measurements. For example, NASA has been looking into the use of a probe which can be dropped vertically through a drill hole to make cross-sectional measurements. The technique is similar to that used in oil-well survey. Advanced versions of ALSEP stations conducting remote observations over an extended period have also been studied.

Missions of this kind will entail double Saturn 5 launchings to place first an unmanned lunar module/shelter on the Moon and second the manned lunar module. The first will be basically an Apollo lunar module with cargo space, carrying the heavier exploration equipment such as the lunar mobility vehicle and drill. There will be additional storage for oxygen and other essential astronaut support items.

The technique involved is similar to soft-landing the unmanned Surveyor spacecraft on the Moon, except that it requires more precise guidance and control onto the appointed target site. The landing radar of the standard Apollo lunar module, in fact, is an advanced version of the radar altimeter and Doppler velocity sensor (RADVS) used in the Surveyor programme. It provides precise measurement of the spacecraft's altitude and velocity relative to the lunar surface during descent and this information is integrated with that of other sensors, computers and sub-systems, to produce a soft landing with or without astronaut overriding control. Therefore, the Apollo system is already fully automated and can be readily adapted to meet the requirements of unmanned supply missions.

After the lunar module/shelter has landed on the Moon it remains quiescent, awaiting the arrival of the manned lunar module which can be launched up to 3 months later. The aim of extended lunar operations is a 2-week stay, with one such mission per year beginning in the early 1970s.

Lifting-body Research Vehicles

Once manned orbiting laboratories are in regular operation, the task of keeping them regularly supplied with men and provisions will demand new spacecraft techniques in order to achieve the necessary economy of operation and flexibility of control. The obvious requirement is a spacecraft which, following a supply mission, can be made to control its descent in such a manner that it returns to land at an airbase. A possible solution to this problem is the lifting-body spacecraft.

Northrop M2-F2 and HL-10 (page 96)

The idea of lifting bodies originated in 1957 with Dr Alfred J. Eggers, Jr, then Assistant Director for Research and Development Analysis and Planning at Ames Research Center. The concept depends on attaining aerodynamic stability and lift from specially shaped bodies without the use of wings. After using orbital energy and aerodynamic lift for hypersonic in-flight manœuvres, the craft must be capable of landing at jet-fighter speeds on a runway following a glide approach.

Theoretical analyses and experimental wind-tunnel development of lifting bodies initially centred on a number of half-cone designs to determine optimum shapes. Specifically, these had to provide sufficiently high lift-drag ratios to allow manœuvring at hypersonic speeds in the thin upper air. To reduce heating during atmospheric re-entry, the nose of the half-cone was blunted after the practice of ballistic missiles. Fins were added to provide stability and control surfaces for manœuvre. A seemingly endless repetition of conceiving, testing, changing, testing, modifying, and testing was required before experimental results began to satisfy the desired, theory-based requirements.

The first manned lifting-body vehicle to fly was the M2-F1 built of plywood and tubular steel. It was merely towed aloft by a C-47 aircraft and released for a glide landing. Nevertheless, this low-cost research effort, conducted at NASA's Flight Research Center, helped to confirm that sufficient lift could be generated at low speeds for a pilot to manœuvre his craft and select his landing site.

The encouraging results led in mid-1964 to NASA awarding contracts to the Norair Division of Northrop Corporation for two 'heavyweight' lifting bodies, the M2-F2 and the HL-10. The latter concept was originated and tested at the NASA Langley Research Center in Hampton, Virginia. The M2-F2 was delivered in June 1965 and the HL-10 in January 1966.

Although they appear similar, these craft are really quite different in configuration. The M2-F2 is a flat-topped, rounded-bottomed, half-conical design with two vertical stabilizers at the rear. Its empty weight is about 5,000 lb. The half-conical HL-10 has a flat bottom, a rounded top, and three stabilizers. The empty weight is 5,265 lb.

There are also differences in control technique. The M2-F2 has two vertical rudders for yaw control which can also act as speed brakes. A single full-span flap on the underside of the boat tail serves for control in pitch. A pair of split horizontal flaps on the upper rear section of the body, if moved differentially, induce roll; if moved together they apply control in pitch and trim.

The HL-10 has a thick elevon (combined elevator and aileron) on each side of the centre fin for pitch and roll; on the centre fin

itself is a split rudder for yaw and speed-brake control. Each
elevon has an upper surface flap and both outer fins have two
trailing-edge surfaces which can be controlled to vary base
drag.

After delivery to the Flight Research Center, instrumentation
was installed in both vehicles for testing in the full-scale wind
tunnel at Ames, after which the craft were returned for minor
modifications.

First glide test of the M2-F2 with the test-pilot Milton O.
Thompson at the controls was made above the Mojave Desert
on 12 July 1966, following release from a B-52 parent aircraft at
450 m.p.h. and 45,000 ft altitude. After separating the lifting
body was first made to perform a straight-ahead glide. The pilot
then made a 90° left turn followed by another straight leg during
which he began a flare manœuvre at about 25,000 ft altitude in
simulation of a landing approach. He then made another 90° left
turn to position the lifting body on the approach path to the
landing site on Rogers Dry Lake. At 1,200 ft Thompson began
the flare manœuvre to slow his rate of descent from about 250
ft/sec. to less than 10 ft/sec., the planned vertical velocity at
touchdown. Landing was made at about 170 m.p.h., the flight
lasting about 4 min.

Four throttleable hydrogen peroxide rockets were fitted to
provide up to 400 lb of thrust each to assist flare-out on the landing
approach. They were not necessary in the initial flight as the
M2-F2 handled so well.

A similar initial glide test was performed by the HL-10 on 22
December 1966, with Bruce Peterson at the controls. After release
from the B-52 at 45,000 ft over the Mojave Desert, two 90° left
turns and a practice flare-out were followed by another perfectly
controlled landing.

Both the M2-F2 and the HL-10 were later fitted with four-
chamber 8,000-lb thrust Thiokol XLR-11 rocket engines burning liquid oxygen and alcohol. This allowed testing from the B-52
to be extended to altitudes of 80,000 ft and speeds of about 1,000
m.p.h. On either side of the rocket engine in the HL-10 is a
1,000-lb thrust hydrogen peroxide landing-assist rocket.

Martin SV-5 series (page 96)

Parallel experiments with lifting-body research craft have been made by the US Air Force. A piloted vehicle, known as the SV-5P, built under contract by the Baltimore Division of the Martin Company, was supplied to the Aeronautical Division of US Systems Command, Wright-Patterson Air Force Base, in 1967. The project formed part of the PILOT (Piloted Lowspeed Test) programme which stemmed from the USAF's Spacecraft Technology and Advanced Re-Entry Test (START) programme.

The purpose of the SV-5P was to explore the flight characteristics of wingless lifting bodies from supersonic speeds of about Mach 2 down to landing speeds of between 120 and 150 m.p.h. Weighing approximately 5,000 lb unfuelled, it has the appearance of a bulbous wedge, curving at the top, flat on the bottom with angled vertical stabilizers.

There are eight aerodynamic control surfaces, two upper and two lower flaps and two split rudders on each of the two outer stabilizers. The upper rudders control the vehicle in yaw. Pitch and roll are controlled by the upper and lower flaps acting as elevons. The lower rudders are not controlled by the pilot; they are merely trim surfaces positioning themselves automatically according to the vehicle's speed.

After a series of glide tests from a B-52, powered flights were being made using a Thiokol XLR-11 rocket engine. Flight tests, conducted by a joint Air Force–NASA team at Edwards Air Force Base, entailed the SV-5P being flown to altitudes of about 100,000 ft and Mach 2 speed.

Martin built another vehicle for the purpose of training pilots in the low-speed handling of lifting bodies. This, the SV-5J, is powered by a turbojet and takes off under its own power.

Meanwhile, rocket launching of sub-scale lifting re-entry vehicles had already begun using half-cone shapes with small delta wings. A radiation-cooled glide-vehicle called ASSET (Aerothermodynamic Structural Systems Environment Test) successfully completed its sixth and last hypersonic flight in February 1965. Each was a 'flying laboratory' containing over 140 measuring instruments. Although only 68 in. long and 58 in.

span, they were fitted with a parachute system, flotation gear, and recovery aids.

Experiments with ASSET vehicles were followed by tests from Vandenberg Air Force Base of the SV-5D. Basically, this was a sub-scale representation of the low-speed piloted SV-5P launched by Atlas-F to orbital altitude and hypersonic speeds. The first of four SV-5Ds, launched on 21 December 1966, was lost after re-entering (according to telemetry data received) in the pre-scribed recovery area midway between the Hawaiian and Philippine Islands. This initial flight was largely to prove basic systems; three additional launchings involved manœuvring the SV-5D and checking its response to ground commands.

Only 7 ft long and 4 ft wide, the SV-5D was flat-bottomed with a rounded top and two vertical stabilizers. It had a self-contained guidance system .with nitrogen reaction jets for control before re-entry and a pair of hinged flaps above and below the tail providing pitch and roll axis control in the atmosphere.

After rocket-launching the tiny vehicle re-entered the atmosphere at speeds approaching orbital velocity. Despite the fact that aerodynamic heating could raise the temperature of critical areas of the exterior to over 1,650° C, the internal structure was made conventionally in aluminium alloy. Its secret was an all-enveloping heat shield applied on a honeycomb structure. The material, a Martin-developed silicone ablative, charred slowly to dissipate frictional heating and in so doing protected the vehicle and its equipment.

This was quite different from the expanding skins of refractory metals proposed for earlier lifting spacecraft such as the celebrated Boeing Dyna-Soar.* The SV-5D's ablative coating was sufficiently flexible to absorb the stresses resulting from abrupt temperature changes. Thickness of the shield material ranged from 0·8 to 2·75 in. and was designed to limit temperature of the basic structure to 204° C. Particularly vulnerable areas of the craft – the nose and underside of the control flaps – were covered by a carbon phenolic ablative material.

* See *Astronautics in the Sixties*, by K. W. Gatland, Iliffe Books Ltd., pp. 326–337.

Vital electronic equipment was protected by a simple sweat-cooling device developed by Martin engineers. Weighing only 19 lb, its only moving parts were five squib valves.

The scheme involved fitting a shallow container filled with highly absorbent wicking material to the base or sides of five electronic components. Each cold plate filled with water was connected through a squib valve to an overboard exhaust tube. When internal temperature began to rise, at a fixed value the squib valves were fired, venting the cold plates to the near-vacuum outside the spacecraft.

At this low pressure, equipment heat boiled the water in the wicks at a much lower temperature than the $100°C$ required at sea-level. The resulting steam flowed through the exhaust space and was dumped overboard.

A wire screen in each of the cold plates provided passageways for the steam to reach the exhaust pipe. The entire cooling system held approximately 1 lb of water. Operating for 30 min. it was capable of removing 1,000 BTUs.

Recovery of the spacecraft involved a precise sequence of actions. Control flaps on the underside were used to manœuvre the craft during hypersonic flight. At subsonic speeds prior to recovery flaps on the top surface, between the stabilizers, were brought into play.

After speed had dropped to about Mach 2 in the recovery area some 4,800 miles downrange from Vandenberg the SV-5D released a drogue parachute; this was followed by deployment of the main landing parachute at about 45,000 ft. Then, as the craft drifted down, it was either air-snatched by the trailing cable booms of a C-130 recovery aircraft or it descended into the sea.

Experiments to date have reinforced the view that a lifting-body spacecraft will be successful in generating sufficient lift and control for a pilot to select his landing point from a wide range of opportunities when returning from orbit. Continuing research has identified a number of supplementary advantages. Elimination of wings markedly reduces structural and heating problems; the body shape provides a large internal volume with a small surface area. The blunt shapes lend themselves more readily to the use of ablative materials for heat dissipation, and lifting-body manœuvrability permits lower deceleration rates and reduced temperatures under re-entry conditions.

Lifting-body spacecraft are considered potentially useful for a variety of future missions. Examples range from spacecraft inspection and repair to search and rescue, reconnaissance and the re-supply of manned space stations. They may also be applied as the upper stages of recoverable launch systems.

Military Uses of Space

Although nuclear weapons were banned from outer space under United Nations treaty in 1967, reconnaissance and surveillance activity from orbit continues to be intensively developed. The technique has steadily evolved from long-established aerial methods.

Many types of military aircraft have been used for reconnaissance duties which operate near the borders of sovereign territory using oblique-angle cameras and radar. Often electronic equipment is carried to eavesdrop on defence communications and surveillance and missile radars. The technique is widely used by both East and West.

Perhaps the most famous reconnaissance aircraft was the Lockheed U-2 which broke established convention by infringing Soviet airspace between 1956 and 1960.

The U-2 prototype first flew in 1955. Three U-2As were delivered to the USAF and ten to NASA by mid-1956. Early U-2As had optional pinion tanks increasing range to 2,600 miles; later U-2As had a 'wet' wing with full-span integral tanks, as did the U-2B introduced in 1959. The USAF aircraft were operated by the 4080th Strategic Reconnaissance Wing at Laughlin Air Force Base.

The NASA aircraft began reconnaissance of Soviet territories in 1956, continuing until 1 May 1960 when Gary Powers's U-2B was lost near Sverdlovsk (see page 105). Another fell to a Guideline missile over Cuba in 1962, and at least four Chinese Nationalist Air Force U-2s have been brought down over Red China.

U-2s also operated by NASA have been used for gust research, and by Strategic Air Command for radar calibration flights. The WU-2A is for high-altitude air sampling to determine radio-activity levels, and the U-2D – a two-seater – was built for missile monitoring.

Samos (page 38)

After the U-2B was lost over the Soviet Union on 1 May 1960, attention turned increasingly to space techniques. The USAF's Samos (Satellite and Missile Observation System) programme began with an unsuccessful launch on 11 October 1960. Samos 2, launched from Point Arguello, California, on 31 January 1961 by an Atlas-Agena A, entered a retrograde orbit, inclined at 97°24′ to the Equator, ranging between 295 and 340 miles. The 4,100-lb spacecraft included the Agena stage of the launch vehicle, the nose-section containing 'photographic and related test equipment'.

Many Samos-type vehicles were subsequently launched under security classification. Orbits of operational vehicles sometimes dipped within 100 miles of 'target' areas in the Soviet Union. Photographic equipment supplied by Eastman Kodak was reported to have a television sub-system and data-recovery link. Processed film was ejected from the spacecraft in General Electric re-entry capsules, using recovery techniques similar to those developed in the USAF's Discoverer programme. A Ferret electronic eavesdropping system was also carried in some vehicles capable of monitoring communications, radar, and other electronic emissions from the Earth's surface.

These techniques are believed to have played a large part in establishing Soviet-bloc developments in terms of cosmodromes, missile sites, nuclear development, and industrial expansion generally. Nuclear and missile developments in Sinkiang Province of Communist China attracted special interest. Photographic results are believed good enough to resolve ground objects 3 to 4 ft across.

Similar techniques are thought to have been developed by the Soviet Union, using recoverable spacecraft in the Cosmos series.

In this situation we are coming remarkably close to a proposal made by General Eisenhower at Geneva on 21 July 1955. To reduce danger and relax tension between East and West, he suggested the US and USSR should accord each other freedom of aerial reconnaissance, 'where you can make all the pictures you choose and take them home to your country to study; you to provide exactly the same facilities to us'.

At the time the idea was firmly rejected by the Soviet authorities. But with mutual reconnaissance by satellite now taking place from the 'no-man's-land' of space, in effect this policy is now actively in force.

Manned Orbiting Laboratory (pages 38, 39)

Further development of reconnaissance and surveillance techniques has since been concentrated by the USAF on the Manned Orbiting Laboratory (MOL) which received President Johnson's approval on 25 August 1965. The development programme comprised unmanned test launchings followed by five manned flights in which pairs of Air Force astronauts were to remain in space for periods of up to 30 days. Launchings were being made both from Cape Kennedy in Florida and Vandenberg Air Force Base in California, with USAF personnel performing control and tracking duties.

The stated objective of the 1,500,000,000 dollars (£535·7 m.) programme is to extend reconnaissance and surveillance activity using the most advanced optical and electronic sensors. The astronauts will be available both to monitor equipment, conduct observations, and perform adjustments and repairs.

The space laboratory itself takes the form of a 41-ft by 10-ft diameter cylinder built by Douglas Aircraft Company. This is divided into two compartments of approximately equal size. One provides crew quarters with some 400 ft^3 of volume for each astronaut. The other is the laboratory section. The vehicle depends on a helium–oxygen atmosphere at 5 to 7·5 p.s.i. allowing the men to work without pressure suits.

Mounted in the extreme nose is a specially adapted Gemini spacecraft in which the astronauts return to Earth after the mission. The men pass between the two vehicles by means of a hatch in Gemini's heat shield. An initial test of the launch system and Gemini spacecraft was made on 3 November 1966, when a Titan 3C lifted off from Cape Kennedy. The launch vehicle – nearly 50 ft taller than earlier versions – included a modified Titan 2 propellant tank and a reconditioned Gemini capsule. The fuel tank allowed study of aerodynamic and other loads acting on the lengthened vehicle. As the vehicle climbed towards orbit, the unmanned Gemini spacecraft was ejected to make a sub-orbital return into the atmosphere and was safely recovered from the Atlantic. The heat shield, which had been modified to include the access hatch, was found to be in excellent condition. The capsule itself had previously made a successful sub-orbital flight on 19 January 1965, as part of the Gemini development programme.

Definitive MOL vehicles were developed under security classification at the Douglas Missile and Space Systems Division at Huntington Beach, California. The laboratory includes an Environmental Control System with tanks for the cryogenic storage of helium and oxygen; there are also oxygen–hydrogen fuel-cells for electrical power supply. A waste management system provides hygienic facilities necessary to maintain proper living conditions for the laboratory crew.

The fully active attitude control system, using hypergolic propellants, depends on two sets of thrusters. One generates a minimum of 100 lb thrust and the other at least 25 lb.

Experimental equipment used in the laboratory section includes high-resolution TV cameras, search radar, and ultra-sensitive infra-red and ultra-violet sensors capable of registering the exhaust signatures of ground-launched missiles.

Various techniques studied by the USAF Space Systems Division, in conjunction with US industry, in setting up the experimental programme were as follows: Image velocity assessment, including acquisition and tracking of ground targets, space targets, and targets of opportunity on land and sea (IBM); Electromagnetic signal detection (Airborne Instrument Laboratory); Remote manœuvring unit (Ling-Temco-Vought); Autonomous navigation (Hughes Aircraft Company); Multi-band spectral observation (Aerojet-General); Sea surveillance (General Electric, Grumman and TRW Systems); and Assembly and erection of large structures (e.g. antennae) in space (Goodyear). The General Electric Company of the USA, at Valley Forge, has the task of co-ordinating and developing chosen experiments. The US Navy also has an interest in the project and indeed many observers believe that the major justification for a follow-on MOL programme in the early 1970s may hinge on the sea surveillance role. Some of the most highly secret work is believed to involve the possibility of detecting nuclear-powered submarines by small temperature differences in the water.

The MOL launch vehicle is the Titan 3M, which includes the basic Martin Titan core with two 10-ft diameter UTC solid-boosters. The seven-segment boost units complete with extended forward closures stand 110 ft tall. This compares with the 86 ft length of the original five-segment boosters used on Titan 3C.

THE LAUNCH VEHICLES

The following is a summary of basic data relating to launch vehicles used in manned space programmes. Weights, thrusts and dimensions are approximate and may not be typical of all vehicles of the same type. Dimensions and weights do not include the spacecraft unless specifically stated.

ATLAS D (pages 30 and 31)

Launch vehicle for Mercury spacecraft (Earth-orbit)

One-and-a-half stage vehicle 69 ft 6 in. long × 10 ft diameter; two Rocketdyne LR89NA5+one Rocketdyne LR105NA5, total thrust 367,000 lb (2 × 154,000 lb × 130 sec.; 1 × 57,000 lb × 275 sec. sustainer), balance of thrust contributed by two small vernier engines for trajectory and final velocity control; propellant—liquid oxygen/kerosene (RP-1); total weight 256,000 lb.

ATLAS-AGENA D (pages 42 and 45)

Launch vehicle for Agena Docking Target (Gemini programme)

Two-stage vehicle (second stage serving also as docking target).

Stage one: (Atlas SLV) 77 ft long × 10 ft diameter; two Rocketdyne LR89NA7+one Rocketdyne LR105NA7; total thrust 389,000 lb (2 × 165,000 lb boost engines, 1 × 57,000 lb sustainer, balance of thrust contributed by two small vernier engines for trajectory and final velocity control); propellant—liquid oxygen/kcroscnc (RP-1); total weight 260,000 lb.

*Stage two: (Agena D) 36 ft 3 in. long (including nose shroud) × 5 ft diameter; one Bell 8096 rocket engine, maximum thrust 16,000 lb; propellant—inhibited red fuming nitric acid (IRFNA)/unsymmetrical dimethyl hydrazine (UDMH); secondary propulsion system (2 × 200 lb and 2 × 16 lb thrust) propellant—MON (mixed oxides of nitrogen)/UDMH. Total weight (fuelled in orbit) 7,000 lb.

*Serves double role as second stage launcher and orbital spacecraft with re-startable rocket system.

REDSTONE (page 31)

Launch vehicle for Mercury spacecraft (sub-orbital)

Single-stage vehicle 58 ft long × 70 in. diameter, one Rocketdyne A-6 rocket engine, thrust 78,000 lb; propellant—liquid oxygen/75% ethyl alcohol and 25% water.

SOVIET FIRST-GENERATION ICBM

Launch vehicle for Vostok spacecraft

According to submission to the Fédération Aéronautique International in May 1961, on the authorization of the Central Chkalov Aviation Club, the multi-stage rocket 'had six engines at the moment of launching with a total thrust of 20 million horse power'. At the 3rd International Space Science Symposium in Washington, 3 May 1962, Major Gherman Titov said Vostok 'was put in orbit by a multistage booster having six liquid-propellant engines. Total maximum thrust of all stages is 600,000 kg (1,323,000 lb)'.

Launch vehicle for Voskhod spacecraft (page 29)

The same type of launch vehicle was up-rated to launch the heavier multi-man spacecraft using a total of seven rocket engines with an aggregate thrust of 650,000 kg. (1,433,250 lb).

TITAN 2 (pages 36 and 37)

Launch vehicle for Gemini spacecraft

Stage one: 63 ft long × 10 ft diameter; two Aerojet-General LR87AJ7 rocket engines, total thrust 430,000 lb; propellant—nitrogen tetroxide (N_2O_4)/Aerozine 50, a half-and-half combination of hydrazine and unsymmetrical dimethyl hydrazine (UDMH).

Stage two: 27 ft long × 10 ft diameter; one Aerojet-General LR91AJ7 rocket engine, thrust 100,000 lb; propellant—nitrogen tetroxide (N_2O_4)/Aerozine 50.

TITAN 3M (page 37)

Launch vehicle for Manned Orbiting Laboratory (MOL)

Lateral boosters: 110 ft long × 10 ft diameter; United Technology Center seven-segment; thrust exceeding 1,250,000 lb each; propellant—solid.

Core vehicle: modified two-stage Titan 2. Thrust first stage: 430,000 lb; second stage 100,000 lb.

UPRATED SATURN 1 (page 64)

Launch vehicle for Apollo spacecraft (Earth-orbit test)

Two-stage vehicle 141 ft long.

Stage one (S-IB): 80 ft long × 21 ft 6 in. diameter; eight Rocketdyne H-1 rocket engines, total thrust 1,600,000 lb; propellant—liquid oxygen/kerosene (RP-1); total weight 1,006,000 lb (84,000 lb dry).

Stage two (S-IVB): 58 ft long × 21 ft 8 in. diameter; one Rocketdyne J-2 rocket engine, thrust 200,000 lb × 470 sec.; propellant—liquid oxygen/liquid hydrogen; total weight 253,000 lb (23,000 lb dry). The instrument unit (containing guidance systems, telemetry and power supply batteries and inverters) is mounted directly above the second stage in a 3-ft deep compartment.

SATURN 5 (page 64)

Launch vehicle for Apollo spacecraft (Lunar mission)

Stage one: (*S-IC*) 138 ft long × 33 ft diameter; five Rocketdyne F-1 rocket engines, total thrust 7,500,000 lb × 150 sec.; propellant—liquid oxygen/kerosene (RP-1); total weight 4,687,000 lb (287,000 lb dry).

Stage two: (*S-II*) 81 ft 6 in. long × 33 ft diameter; five Rocketdyne J-2 rocket engines, total thrust 1,000,000 lb × 390 sec.; propellant—liquid oxygen/liquid hydrogen; total weight 1,005,000 lb (75,000 lb dry).

Stage three: (*S-IVB*) 58 ft 8 in. long × 21 ft 8 in. diameter; one Rocketdyne J-2 rocket engine, thrust 200,000 lb × 480 sec.; propellant—liquid oxygen/liquid hydrogen; total weight 251,900 lb (21,900 lb dry).

The instrument unit (containing guidance systems, telemetry and power supply batteries and inverters) is mounted directly above the third stage; total weight is 3,500 lb. Payload: Lunar module 30,000 lb; service module 46,000 lb; command module 10,000 lb; launch escape system 6,600 lb.

GLOSSARY OF SPACE TERMS

Ablation	erosion of a solid body (e.g. a spacecraft's heat shield) by a high-velocity, high-temperature gas stream
'Abort'	emergency termination of a rocket launching
Acceleration	rate of change of velocity
Apogee	that point in a terrestrial orbit farthest from the Earth
Astronautics	the science and technology of spaceflight
Ballistic trajectory	path followed by vehicle in unpowered flight
Booster	propulsion unit used in initial stage of flight

Chaff metal-foil strips ejected from a tracked space-vehicle to enhance the radar response

Cosmonaut Soviet term for an astronaut; a space-traveller

Cryogenic propellant one that, at atmospheric pressure, has a boiling-point below 0° C of the liquified gas (e.g. liquid oxygen, liquid hydrogen)

Escape velocity velocity needed to escape from a given point in a gravitational field (e.g. 6·95 miles/sec. to escape from the Earth's surface)

Free-fall motion of a body moving in a gravitational field without power (see *weightlessness*)

Fuel-cell battery in which chemical reaction is used directly to produce electricity

g symbol for the acceleration of a freely moving body due to gravity at the surface of the Earth

Gimbal mechanical frame for a gyroscope or power-plant, usually with two perpendicular axes of rotation

Hypergolic term applied to a fuel and oxidant which ignite spontaneously on contact

Lunar of or pertaining to the Moon

Mach number ratio of the speed of a vehicle to the local speed of sound, approximately 750 m.p.h. at sea-level

Multi-stage rocket a rocket having two or more stages which jettison sequentially

Orbit path of a body relative to its primary

Orbital period time taken by an orbiting body to complete one orbit of its primary

Orbital velocity speed of a body following closed or open orbit, generally applied to elliptical or near circular orbits, e.g. close to Earth about 18,000 m.p.h.

Perigee that point in a terrestrial orbit closest to the Earth

Probe unmanned vehicle sent into space to gather information by means of instruments

Propellant   liquid or solid substance or substances burned in a rocket engine to produce thrust

Re-entry   return of a space vehicle into the Earth's atmosphere

Rendezvous   planned meeting between two spacecraft in orbit

Retro-rocket   rocket fired against direction of motion to reduce speed

Shingles   thin interleaved plates of metal used as outer heat-resistant skin

Solar   of or pertaining to the Sun

Solar cell   silicon wafer that converts sunlight directly into electricity

Solar wind   constant stream of ionized gas atoms, mostly hydrogen, from the Sun

Stage   self-contained propulsion system in a launch vehicle which has stages operating sequentially

Telemetry   system for relaying data from a spacecraft's instruments by radio to a ground receiving station

Terrestrial   of or pertaining to the Earth

Umbilical   flexible connector which conveys power to a spacecraft and/or launch vehicle before take-off; connector supplying an astronaut during extra-vehicular activity

Ullage   that volume in a tank not occupied by propellant

Ullage rocket   propulsion unit applied under weightless conditions to force propellant to outlets in the bottom end of a tank, for purposes of engine re-starting, by reactive effect

Weightlessness   state experienced in ballistic flight – in orbit or free-fall – when a body experiences no mechanical stress because the gravitational attraction is opposed by equal and opposite inertial forces

Zero-g   condition of weightlessness

INDEX

Numerals in **bold** refer to illustrations

Agena Docking Target **42, 43, 45, 50, 51,** 169–71, 173–7

Agena Target Docking Adapter (ATDA) **45,** 166, 169, 171, 172

Aldrin, Edwin 176–8, 214

Animal experiments 99, 107, 109, 115, 137–9, 144, 145, 149

Apollo Applications Programme (AAP) 226–38, **228–30**

Apollo disaster 179–81, 219, 220

Apollo spacecraft
  adapter module **65,** 184, 221
  command module **66, 68, 75, 88–91,** 179, 180, 217–19
  Earth return **84–7, 90, 91,** 194, 195
  first unmanned tests 179
  launch escape system **66, 69, 78,** 218
  lunar landing **81–3,** 187–9, **222**
  lunar module **65, 67, 71–5, 79–85,** 184–90, 192, 221, **222,** 225, 226
  lunar orbit rendezvous 193
  lunar take-off **84,** 192, 193
  programme 179, 182–95, 217–26
  service module **66, 87–9,** 184, 185, 194, 220, 221
  transposition and docking **79, 80,** 184

Apollo Telescope Mount (ATM) **228–30,** 233–5

Astronaut Manœuvring Unit (AMU) **14, 59,** 171, 173, 176

Armstrong, Neil A. 169, 170, 214

Atlas-Agena D 169, 248

Atlas D **31,** 150, 169, 248

Atlas SM-65 103

Baikonur cosmodrome **28,** 103, 111, 122, 133, 136

Belyaev, Pavel 133, 135, 136, 214

BIS Lunar Spaceship (study) **92,** 216, 217

Borman, Frank 167, 214

British Interplanetary Society 192

Bykovsky, Valery 122, 126, 127, 140, 214

Carpenter, M. Scott 153–5, 214

Central Intelligence Agency (CIA) 104

Cernan, Eugene A. 172, 173, 214

Chaffee, Roger 179, 180

Collins, Michael 174, 214

Conrad, Charles Peter 162, 174, 214

Cooper, L. Gordon 156–9, 162, 164, 165, 214

Cosmos 47 136

Cosmos 110 137–8

Cunningham, Walter 181

Deep Space Network (DSN) 184

Docking, First space 169, 170

Eisele, Donn F. 181

Extra-vehicular experiment, First US **53,** 161, 162

Extra-vehicular experiment, First Soviet 133–5

Feoktistov, Konstantin 131, 132, 214

Food for astronauts 116, 119, 120, 122, 124, 150, 157, 158, 209

Fuel-cells 163, 185

Gagarin, Yuri 110–13, 121, 128, 132, 139, 140, 214

Gemini spacecraft **14, 44, 50, 56, 57,** 159–65, 207, **208,** 210, 211, 213, 214

Gemini, Emergency escape from **46**, **47**

Gemini GT-3 160, 214
   GT-4 161, 162, 214
   GT-5 162-6, 214
   GT-6 166-8, 214
   GT-7 167-9, 214
   GT-8 169, 170, 214
   GT-9 171-3, 214
   GT-10 173, 174, 214
   GT-11 174-6, 214
   GT-12 176-8, 214

Gemini re-entry and landing **48**, **49**
German rocket collective in USSR **28**, 100
Glenn, John 150-2, 214
Glushko, Valentin P. 130
Gordon, Richard F. **52**, 174, 175, 214
Grissom, Virgil I. 148, 149, 160, 179, 180, 214

HL-10 lifting body **96**, 238-40
Human skin experiment 107, 108

Inter-Continental Ballistic Missile, First Soviet 97, 104
Inter-Continental Ballistic Missile, First US designs for 103

Kapustin Yar **28**, 102, 103
Kennedy Space Center **60-3**, 182
Komarov, Vladimir 131, 139-40, 214
Korolev, Sergei Pavlovich 130, 131

Leonov, Alexei 133-6, 214
Little Joe 142
Lovell, James 167, 168, 176, 214

M2-F2 lifting body **96**, 238-40
Manned Orbiting Laboratory (MOL) **38**, **39**, 246-8
Manned Orbiting Research Laboratory (MORL) **93**, 236
Manned Spacecraft Center 183, 187
McDivitt, James A. 161, 214

Mercury astronauts 142, 214
Mercury spacecraft **30-5**, **40**, **41**, 143, 145-55, 205-7, **208**, 214
Mercury MR-3 147, 214
   MR-4 148, 149, 214
   MA-6 150-2, 214
   MA-7 153-5, 214
   MA-8 155, 156, 214
   MA-9 156-9, 214
Merritt Island **60-2**, 165, 182

NASA, Establishment of 141
Nikolayev, Andrian 117-21, 140, 214

Orbital workshop 227, **228**, **229**, **230**, 231, 232, 233, 235

Photography from orbit **50-2**, **54**, **55**, **61**, 164, 165, 175, 209
Pobeda (Victory) rocket 102
Popovich, Pavel 117-21, 140, 214

Radar Evaluation Pod (REP) 163, 167
Radar tracking 102, 184
Radio tracking 98
Redstone **31**, 143, 145, 249

Samos **38**, 245
Saturn 5 **64**, **65**, **77**, 182, 183, 250
Schirra, Walter M. 155-66, 181, 214
Scott, David R. 169-71, 214
Shepard, Alan B. 147, 148, 214
Slayton, Donald K. 142
SNAP-27 190, **224-5**
Soviet Pacific rocket tests 105, 106
Soviet State Commission on long-range rockets 101
Soviet V-2 101, 102
Soyuz 1 139, 140
Spacecraft 1 105
Spacecraft 2 107
Spacecraft 3 109
Spacesuits **58**, **76**, 132, 168, 189, 199, 203

Sputnik 1 **18**, 98, 99
Sputnik 2 **18**, 98, 99
Sputnik 3 **18**, 100
Stafford, Thomas P. 166, 172, 214
'Stellar Village' 129
SV-5 series **96**, 241–3

Tereshkova, Valentina 123–9, 140,
    159, 214
Titan 2 **36**, **37**, 250
Titan 3C **39**, 247, 248
Titan 3M **37**, 248, 250
Titov, Gherman 115–17, 123, 214

U-2 **38**, 104, 105, 244, 245
Uprated Saturn 1 **64**, 179, 250

Visibility from space 129, 158, 165,
    166
Voskhod 1 131–3
Voskhod 2 **19**, **27**, 133
Voskhod launch vehicle 250
Vostok 1 **17**, **19–26**, 110–15
Vostok 2 115–17
Vostok 3 117–19
Vostok 4 117–19
Vostok 5 121, 122
Vostok 6 123–7
Vostok launch vehicle 250

X-15 **94**, **95**, 203–5

Yegorov, Boris 131, 138, 139, 214
Young, John W. 160, 174, 214